Robert Lincoln

MORE FUN WITH CHESS MINIATURES

540 PUZZLES FOR TYRO AND VETERAN

US CHESS FEDERATION

NEW WINDSOR, NY 12553

914-562-8350 • 800-388-KING (5464) • WWW.USCHESS.ORG

US Chess Federation
3054 Route 9W, New Windsor, NY 12553
914-562-8350 • 800-388-KING (5464)
www.uschess.org

©2000 USCF
© R A LINCOLN, 2000
ISBN 0-9700852-0-6

Typesetting and Design
by the US Chess Federation.

Printed in Canada.

THIS BOOK IS DEDICATED TO THE MEMORY OF

Helen P. Bode (1916–1978)

Because of her, I became inspired with a zeal for learning.

ACKNOWLEDGEMENTS

F. Scott Fitzgerald once said: "There are no second acts." Well, sometimes there are, and I am privileged to present this successor to *Fun with Chess Miniatures*. Thanks to the good offices of Glenn Petersen and his ever-helpful staff at Chess Life, *More Fun with Chess Miniatures* is a reality. My ongoing association with this magazine has afforded opportunity to discourse on chess problems freely. It almost seemed inevitable that another book was brewing in the subconscious.

The usual suspects have generously contributed valuable material, ideas, and moral support – Eugene Albert, Barry Barnes, John Beasley, Viktor Chepizhny, Vladimir Kozhakin, Tony Lewis, Michael McDowell, Rui Nascimento, Henk Nijmeijer, John Rice, Colin Russ, Denis Saunders, Ian Shanahan, David Shire, Brian Stephenson, and Paul Valois. My mere appreciation is hardly enough.

A master proofreader was found in the family. My son Jeff possesses a command of language and usage, which I cannot attain.

And to my wife Carol, who soothes over all the rough spots, let us continue forever our journey together.

INTRODUCTION

Herewith is another effort to assemble two-mover chess miniatures not seen before under one cover. I have composed some three hundred problems since the appearance of *Fun with Chess Miniatures*. Quite a few found their way into this collection.

By and large, I was able to amass most of the specimens from newspapers and assorted chess periodicals. But it was still necessary to rely on previous books for certain specific illustrations.

Additional care has gone into eliminating those irksome typos, as my keyboard dexterity is atrocious. Presumably, I have avoided such bloopers as the position with eight men, which crept into the first volume. A handful of my originals may eventually be published elsewhere. Their fate could not be learned upon going to press.

I hope that the commentary will attract newcomers to this specialty form. At the same time, my wish is to not bore established patrons of the miniature.

Smaller problems clearly contain the same merit as much larger ones. The Scots have an expression:

"Guid gear in sma' bulk!"

1. A d'ORVILLE
Problems d'Echecs
Nurnberg, 1842

#2

2. A d'ORVILLE
(v) *Problems d'Echecs*
Nurnberg, 1842

#2

3. P MORPHY
New York Clipper,
1856

#2

4. E B COOK
American Chess Nuts,
1868

#2

5. G N CHENEY
American Chess Nuts,
1868

#2

6. W SHINKMAN
Detroit Free Press,
1880

#2

7. R L'HERMET
Magdeburg Schachzeitung,
1884

#2

8. O WURZBURG
Chess Review,
1936

#2

9. E CAMPONOVO
Basler Nachrichten,
1948

#2

ANCIENT HISTORY

The miniature chess problem arose out of obscure beginnings. Primitive relics survive from hundreds of years ago. But it was not until the nineteenth century that composers advanced on the barest of rudimentary play. Auguste d'Orville was perhaps the first distinct personality from that misty era who bequeathed a significant body of work. Here are two tidbits which indicate just how hesitant these foundling efforts were. **1** has a rook suspended midair. Black is welcome to 1. ... Kxd5 after 1. Be5 when 2. Qb5 concludes.

2 provides far superior tactics. The set flight, 1. ... Ke6, already cowers to 2. Qd6. However, no deliberate fidgeting can preserve this outcome. An agreeable 1. Bf6 alters that prepared extinction in favor of 2. Qc6. One humble queen change comprises a Spartan statement. Nonetheless, this is genuine "mutate."

Any composition by a former world champion is more than an obsolescent tinker-toy. A cornered quarry in **3** faces 1. ... B~ 2. Rxa7, but saving respites remain 1. ... a6! or 1. ... a5! The kamikaze 1. Ra6 seals off those options to enforce a new terminus 1. ... bxa6 2. b7.

Eugene Beauharnais Cook was a legend in his own time. He possessed an astonishing skill for plumbing the depths of any chessic conundrum. Cook's feats of analytical magic served the purpose prior to modern high-speed computers. **4** reveals the germ of his genius. 1. Qd7 keys proceedings by relinquishing a new g5 hiatus in addition to those at g6 and h4. The threat (2. Qg4) disposes of 1. ... Kh4 or 1. ... Kg5, while 2. Qf5 lies in wait for 1. ... Kg6. A line-cut defense, 1. ... g5, self-blocks opening unto 2. Qh7. Although average by today's standard, this frippery still represented a huge stride over predecessors.

Some real puzzle content is hitched to **5.** Black's king will obviously be extricated from total confinement. That lurking rook at g1 gives the game away. Surely 1. g4 has to succeed with the pawn forging ahead after 1. ... Kf4 2. g5. The other choice, 1. ... Kxh4, gets reeled in by 2. Bf6.

William Shinkman, the celebrated "Wizard of Grand Rapids," churned out assorted problems by the bushel. His entrancing **6** would compare favorably among any number of Black promotion concepts. 1. ... d1=S 2. Re1 is no worry, except that spiteful 1. ... d1=Q! bogs White's rook down. 1. Kh2 lopes hither from the forthcoming pin making an eventual 2. Rf2 possible. Acceptance of the gift 1. ... Kxf1 spells 2. Bd3.

7 signifies an early example of Black "pawn string." 1. Qg8 sets up shop for the weakening 1. ... b3 2. Qf8 and 1. ... c3 2. Qa2. Lastly, 1. ... Kb3 walks smack into 2. Rd3. See # 350 for contemporary treatment of a similar formation.

ARISTOCRATS

The term "aristocrat" simply refers to absence of pawns — not the position's merits! White amasses awesome firepower to subdue a lone combatant in **8.** 1. Sc8 puts up important guards to seize 1. ... Kd8 (or 1. ... Ke8) 2. Qe7 and 1. ... Kc7 (or 1. ... Kc6) 2. Qd6. Black's indiscriminate knight moves cost 2. Qa4. The corrective 1. ... Sxc8 incurs dazzling ideal mate via 2. Bb5.

2. Rd5 makes short shrift of bishop removals in **9.** As might be expected, there is no way to maintain this stance. A truly surprising 1. Kb5 pits rejoinders for 1. ... B ~ 2. Rc6 and 1. ... Kd5 2. Rd8. This particular "two-for-one" exchange is an engaging transaction.

10. R T LEWIS
The Problemist,
1981

#2

11. R A LINCOLN
Australian Chess Problem
Magazine, 1997

#2

12. R A LINCOLN
Australian Chess Problem
Magazine, 1997

#2

13. A KAMENIK
Mainzer Allegemeine Zeitung,
1993

#2

14. V KUZMICHEV
Ideal-Mate Review,
1988

#2

15. V MELNICHENKO
6th Place, *Edorove,*
1990

#2

16. A DIKUSAROV
Buletin problemistic,
1989

#2

17. J RICE
Chess Life,
1999

#2

18. T SWEENEY
Chess Life & Review,
1974

#2

ARISTOCRATS (CONT'D)

White contrives another two-for-one barter in **10**. A set 2. Rxe6 awaits any displacement by the Black equestrian on c5. As usual, everything is firmly nailed down. 1. Rd5 is the sensible selection. A different fate, 2. B(x)d7, now attends c-knight's departure, while the freshly unpinned stable buddy must surrender 2. R(x)d8.

One advantage aristocrats produce is ability to gyrate the board around for one's satisfaction. When given a choice, I prefer to put that wicked gonif on the initial array square as in **11**. A logical 1. Kg8? conjectures (2. Qf8), where 1. ... Sg6 falls to 2. Bf7. But Black appropriates a d7 breakout by 1. ... Bxb8! The correct 1. Sc6! ironically awards the same exit gratis. With a dagger aimed at (2. Qe7), the defense thrashes about with futile paroxysms – 1. ... Sg6 2. Qf7, 1. ... Sxc6 2. Bxc6, 1. ... Bd6 2. Qd8, and 1. ... Kd7 2. Qe6.

12 utilizes identical actors mid-board. Once again, the gallant knight lifts guard on a potential flight. 1. Se2 intends to recover protection over e4 with (2. Sc3). Black's little empire is mercilessly overrun — 1. ... Sb1 2. Bf3, 1. ... Se4 2. Sf4, 1. ... Be6 2. Qxe6, and 1. ... Ke4 2. Qd4.

Editors are delighted to get diagrams with a majority of symbols posted on white squares for enhanced legibility. **13** finds all seven men in bold relief. 1. Qf7 is admittedly a bit powerful. Nevertheless, the finishing blows daub an attractive picture. The unlucky king traipses into 1. ... Kxc6 2. Qb7, 1. ... Kc4 2. Qxe6, and 1. ... Kxe4 2. Qf3.

Critics may justifiably denigrate the aggressive opening of **14**. 1. Qg2 does after all deprive two shelves at c2 and d2. But I think the resultant finales fully substantiate an unorthodox start. Black's bishop captures 1. ... Bxc2 to be undone by 2.

Qg5. Otherwise, the ill-starred cleric is rocked by 1. ... Ba2 2. Sxa2. Both cases disport graceful ideal mates.

Black's f5 servitor dutifully fends off violent forays in **15**. 1. ... Bxe6! counters 1. Qxe6? and 1. ... Bg6! efficiently copes with 1. Rxe6? The trusty bishop is a helpless spectator after 1. Qa1! (2. Rxe6). The attacker cares not whether 1. ... Q-file 2. Rf8 or 1. ... Qxf6+ 2. Qxf6.

ASSAULT WITH BATTERIES

Battery mates are a major ingredient in many large scale two-movers. When employed in miniature setting, they tend to focus on intensive exertions. **16** gets things underway with an unfortunate key 1. Rd1 (2. Bxe8). As the targeted bishop motors down the diagonal, White's "firing" piece badgers his every move — 1. ... Bf7 2. Be6, 1. ... Bg6 2. Bf5, and 1. ... Bh5 2. Bg4. 2. Qxd7 guzzles 1. ... Bxd7 and 2. Qc8 stomps attempted rescues such as 1. ... Rb5.

Knights often prove dynamic frontal units. **17** has a tireless cavalier travel to five jumping-off points. First, 1. ... Qf1+ is cross-checked 2. Sf5. Regrettably, there is no set antidote for 1. ... Qa1+! In any event, 1. Ke6 introduces paired threats, (2. Qf2,Qf5), which can be thwarted by six means. 1. ... Qa2+, 1. ... Qe2+, and 1. ... Qa5 are chastised by 2. Sc4, 2. Se4, and 2. Sb5 respectively. 1. ... Qd3 permits 2. Qc8 and 1. ... Qb7 gets scooped off 2. Sxb7. At length, 2. Qxd6 mashes 1. ... Qxd6+. Despite undesirable flaws, this still embodies an impressive demonstration.

18 may seem paltry by comparison. 1. Sd7 regroups to command vital control of e5 and f6. The threat (2. Rxe5) works just as well if the Black king relocates to f5 or g5. The only bona fide defensive gesture is 1. ... e4 2. Rf3.

19. H HULTBERG
Springaren,
1990

#2

20. N NEPTAJEV
Nikolaev-200,
1989

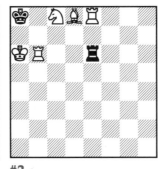

#2

21. V MARKOVSKY
Die Schwalbe,
1995

#2

22. V MARKOVSKY
The Problemist,
1992

#2

23. V MARKOVSKY
2nd HM., *Smena,*
1997

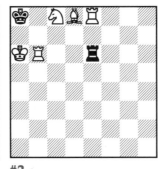

#2

24. R A LINCOLN
Newark Star-Ledger,
1999

#2

25. G JORDON
Freie Presse,
1993

#2

26. RAL
Original

#2

27. V MELNICHENKO
Smena,
1998

#2

ASSAULT WITH BATTERIES (CONT'D)

Solvers will rightfully suspect that **19** will devolve on a castling prank. Both king and bishop are going to lift off to expose the lurking rook. This specific arrangement is known as "half-battery. " 1. Kd2?, menacing (2. Ba3), comes to a juddering halt thanks to 1. ... Bxb7! Therefore the reverse order 1. Ba3! nabs 1. ... Kb1 2. Kd2. And of course 1. ... Bxb7 demands 2. 0-0.

Two plausible rook sallies animate **20.** 1. Rc8? is wholly ineffective against 1. ... Kg6! 1. Rc5? looks better because 2. Sd6 attends to 1. ... Kg6. But Black calmly winkles out by 1. ... Kg8! 1. Sd6! (2. Rc8) wins, whereupon 1. ... Kg6 gets reduced by a "direct" battery, 2. Rc5. 1. ... Kg8 converts the threat to "indirect. " Thus, moves associated with tries are resumed as mates. This phenomenon, the Banny theme, has further renditions in #'s 40, 358, 399, and 400.

White's king stimulates some precise battery play in **21.** Faulty steps are 1. Kd7? Ra7!, 1. Kc5? Rc2+!, and 1. Ke6? Kc8! 1. Kd5! convinces after 1. ... Ra5+ (or 1. ... Ka7) 2. Sb5 and 1. ... Kc8 2. Se6. Yet another dipsy-doodle follows that pretty self-block, 1. ... Ra7, when a pungent 2. Sa6 concludes.

The Black confederates of **22** stymie wayward rook tries. 1. Rd3? (2. Rh3) banks on 1. ... Kh2 2. Rc2 and 1. ... B~ 2. Rh6. However, 1. ... f4! unhinges a bishop lock on h3. 1. Rd2? (2. Rxe6) snatches off 1. ... Bc4+ 2. Rxc4 but also cannot suppress that obdurate 1. ... f4! Only an exact 1. Rc3! (2. Rh3) greases the wheels for 1. ... Kh2 2. Rd2 and 1. ... f4 2. Rh5.

23 must clearly take 1. ... Rxb6+! into account. 1. Se7? (2. Bc7) proposes to punish 1. ... Rxb6+ by 2. Bxb6. The everresourceful rook squeaks out 1. ... Rd6! 1. Be7? (2. S~) narrowly fails to 1. ... Rc6! A befitting 1. Bc7! (2. Se7) has the virtue of neutralizing that last defense. Now the forlorn rook succumbs after 1. ... Rd6 2. Sxd6, 1. ... Rxb6+ 2. Sxb6, and 1. ... Rxe8 2. Rb8. "Unprovided checks," were once considered taboo. Nowadays they are commonly accepted in the ongoing quest for originality.

BAIT AND SWITCH

This group shows problems which are purposefully booby-trapped to delude unwary solvers. White cannot twiddle his filings in **24.** 1. ... e5 (2. Qg6) seems solid, but there is nothing for 1. ... e3! 1. Qc7? (2. Qf4) is the bait allowing 1. ... e5! The switch is 1. Qc4! changing 1. ... e5 2. Qf7 and furnishing 2. Qf4 for 1. ... e3. Finally, 1. ... Ke5 kowtows to 2. Qc5.

The set mates of **25** enjoin prominent attention. 1. ... f4 2. Qd5 and 1. ... Re5 2. Qb4 are appealing, but by no means forced. One may be lulled into 1. Sc2? (2. Qd4), when 1. ... f4! preempts. 1. Sc4! (2. Sd2) stays on the mark. 1. ... f4 returns to crash against (2. Qd3) and 1. ... Re5 gets swallowed 2. Qxe5.

One's natural inclination would be to activate the rook in **26.** 1. Rb5? (2. Ra5) turns out a bust since 1. ... Bb4! Instead, the queen fixes her gaze on (2. Qa5) by 1. b7! First 1. ... Bb6 is flayed 2. Qxb6. Then that onrushing pawn achieves two separate elevations — 1. ... Bb4 2. bxa8=Q and 1. ... Ka7 2. b8=S.

Initially, **27** has that irksome 1. ... Kc4 flight censured by 2. Qe4. A threat must occur as 1. ... b2! will never hurt the defense. 1. Kc7? conjures (2. Sb6), but 1. ... Kc4! becomes rendered perfectly safe. The hero is 1. Sf2! (2. Qe4), where 1. ... Kc4 rambles into a changed fate 2. Qc5. This variation reveals that the b3 pawn's subsidiary pretext for inclusion is to impede egress.

28. V MARKOVSKY
Probleemblad,
1997

#2

29. RAL
Original

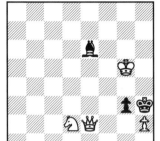

#2

30. V MARKOVSKY
Probleemblad,
1998

#2

31. J ROPETT
*Blumenthal
Schachminiaturen,* 1902

#2

32. V KICHIGIN
Norsk Sjakkblad,
1986

#2

33. K HARCZ
Magyar Sakkvilág
1934

#2

34. M SOARES
*Revista Portuguesa de
Xadrez,* 1937

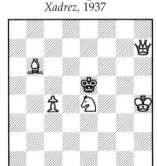

#2

35. S LOVE
The Problemist,
1984

#2

36. R A LINCOLN
Comm., *The Problemist,*
1994

#2

BAIT AND SWITCH (CONT'D)

No one should assume any blame for being gulled into the fallacious 1. Bc6? (2. b4) of **28**. Prospects are promising in view of 1. ... Rb4 2. Qb2 and 1. ... Rxb3 2. Qa5. Liberation arrives from a spunky shutoff 1. ... Rb5! The brighter 1. Qxc4! (2. Qa4) spawns revised continuations to 1. ... Rb4 2. Qc1 and 1. ... Rxb3 2. Qxb3. Another reply, 1. ... Ra8, sanctions 2. Qc5.

Solvers should be bound to notice set replies for self-blocks in **29**. 1. ... gxh2 2. Qf3 and 1. ... g2 2. Qh5 will evidently change since White requires a tangible threat. Sure enough, 1. Sf3 (2. Sg1) transforms 1. ... gxh2 to 2. Qxh2 and 1. ... g2 to 2. Qxe6.

Drastic action is needed for **30** where 1. ... Kc5! flies off with impunity. This dire emergency may tempt the solver to miss predetermined coups for 1. ... Rd5 2. Qxd5 and 1. ... Rc5 2. Qg4. 1. Bd3 (2. Qc4) affably substitutes 1. ... Rd5 2. Qe3 and 1. ... Rc5 2. Qe4. The former refuge, 1. ... Kc5, gets picked up 2. Qd6.

BALANCE OF TRADE

So-called "give-and-take" keys usually involve a favorable, albeit tentative, balance of trade for Black. White filches vacant habitats and offers others in return. In **31**, the free harbor at e6 begs closure. 1. Sf4 (2. Rd5) converts the rook to a tainted gift — 1. ... Kxd4 2. Bf6.

That gaping aperture at g4 clamors for prompt repair in **32**. 1. Bf4 tenders a fake sacrifice which is reclaimed 1. ... Kxf4 2. Rf1. 2. Qg3 cuffs the self-block 1. ... e2 and 1. ... Ke2 slogs into 2. Qxe3.

33 strikes a bargain for Black. 1. Sa4 steals b6 while conferring a4 and c4. The bishop chases 1. ... Ka6 2. Bd3 and 1. ... Kxa4 2. Bd7. 2. Qd7 puts a wrap on 1. ... Kc6.

34 is another two-for-one pact where Black's scurrying freebooter is entitled to three outlets altogether. 1. Sg5 abandons d6 and f6 to cast a perceptive eye on e6. A scathing barrage blisters 1. ... Kd6 2. Qc7, 1. ... Kf6 2. Bd4, and 1. ... Kf4 2. Qe4.

A spectacular revelation emerges from **35**. What I find remarkable is a trim force operating quite capably minus the White queen. 1. Bd7 shifts protection from a6 to b5. Variants are 1. ... a6 2. b4 and 1. ... Ka6 2. Sb4. It takes a moment to really appreciate that both Black moves went to a6. By the same token, both White strokes landed on b4. This is a curious and enviable occurrence rarely seen.

BARNES THEME

The modern two-mover draws chief sustenance from "virtual" play. What doesn't occur is just as consequential as what does in "actual" play. Hence, a whole shorthand method describing set and try patterns has grown profusely. This alphabet soup may seem a puzzling bane to newcomers. But once understood, it becomes an invaluable tool for comprehending difficult mechanisms. The Barnes theme derives its name from Barry Barnes, the distinguished British composer, editor, and popularizer of the art. The enterprise features a moderate paradox. There are double and single threats in tries, with the alternate threat as key. Algebraically it looks like: 1. ? (2. A, B) 1. ... x!, 1. ? (2. A) 1. ... y!, and 1. ! (2. B) **36** displays essential ingredients through a very minimal interpretation. 1. Sd5? (2. Sc7, Sb6) thwarted 1. ... Bd8! 1. Sb5? (2. Sc7) flops because 1. ... Bf4! has 2. ... Bb8! reserved against 2. Rd8+? The last element 1. Sa4! (2. Sb6) thrives where the rook is itching to pounce on 1. ... Bd8 2. Rxd8.

37. RAL
Original

#2

38. R A LINCOLN
(v) *The Problemist,*
1999

#2

39. E KOWALEWSKI
Chess Life,
1959

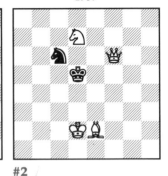

#2

40. H GOCKEL
The Problemist,
1983

#2

41. R BREIGER
The Joy of Mate,
1985

#2

42. W ROSCHER
Dresdner Volkzeitung,
1926

#2

43. R KINTZIG
Magyar Sakkvilág,
1919

#2

44. R A LINCOLN
Newark Star-Ledger,
1998

#2

45. W E PERRY
Canadian Chess Problems,
1890

#2

BARNES THEME (CONT'D)

A trifle more action is enfolded into the aristocratic **37.** 1. Qe3? deploys the thematic pair (2. Qh6,Qg5) where Black expeditiously obtrudes 1. ... Rf4! 1. Qb6? (2. Qh6) improves by evading the rook's range but 1. ... Se6! squats astride the path. A long reach 1. Qg1! (2. Qg5) wins the blue ribbon. Vain stabs at resistance are 1. ... Rg4 2. Qxg4 and 1. ... Se6 2. Qg6.

Flight squares inevitably augment the latitude for more mating variety. **38** has Black effect a pawn "one-two" to cancel tries. 1. Qb5? zeroing in on (2. Qe5,Qd5) encounters 1. ... d6! 1. Qb8? (2. Qe5) gets roughly rejected 1. ... d5! 1. Qb7! (2. Qd5) sponsors answers all around — 1. ... d6 2. Qc8, 1. ... Kd6 2. Qb6, and 1. ... Kf5 2. Qe4. Incidentally, the *raison d'être* for that g4 soldier would appear to bar 1. ... Kf5 exodus after White essays 1. Qb8? Moreover, it is vindicated by the non-thematic, or "cook" try, 1. Qd3? (2. Qd5) where 1. ... d6! suitably frustrates because 2. Qh3? cannot ensue.

BEGINNER'S LUCK

This section is devoted to positions which pose no challenge for experienced solvers. They frequently appear in any number of publications. Their principal merit is giving newcomers to the hobby confidence builders. No seasoned sleuth will expect 1. ... Ke4 2. Bf3 to abide in **39.** 1. Bb5 is quickly scented where 1. ... Ke4 then abdicates to 2. Bxc6 and 1. ... S~ gets vanquished 2. Q(x)e5.

It is apparent that White must stake out runaways to d6 and f6 in **40.** 1. Qb7 shields the seventh rank so that morose, friendless monarch ambles into the jaws of 1. ... Kd6 2. Sf7 and 1. ... Kf6 2. Sg4. Hubert Gockel's problem has a hidden level of virtual play. Only a trained hand will detect 1. Qf3? (2. Sf7) Kd6! and 1. Qc6? (2. Sg4) Kf6! — the Banny theme.

41 is a singular oddity. Even a green rookie will gleefully spot 1. Rg8 (2. B~) without hesitation. Robert Brieger is an endgame composer par excellence. He no doubt tossed off this skimpy item for novice instruction. It can be noted 2. Bd6 issues under three discrete guises — 1. ... Qh7 (necessary double check), 1. ... Qxe6+ (cross-check), and 1. ... Sc7 (necessary pin mate).

42 directs any solver to cap that yawning chasm at e6. The temporary gift of 1. Re4 is a loaner to being swiftly repossessed after 1. ... Kxe4 2. Qd3. Three other deviations tidy up neatly — 1. ... S~ 2. Q(x)c4, 1. ... Kc5 2. Qa5, and 1. ... c5 2. Qb7.

The rook key of **43** may be a fraction harder to settle. That g-knight cannot budge upon pain of 2. R(x)e4. 1. d4 polices movements of the other swaggering pony. The injurious clinker is 1. ... Sd4! Most neophytes would divine 1. Rc4 to handle this contingency with 2. Rc5.

44 is meant to be a user-friendly problem fairly simple to decipher. Only a knight shock will stir those rooks from their somnolent repose. Besides, 1. Qf5 (2. Sf6) is about the only reasonable start. The h7 sentry gets captured after 1. ... Rf7 2. Qxf7 or 1. ... Rf8 2. Qxh7. 1. ... Rh6 stays out of the queen's scope but self-blocks for 2. g6.

The pawnless setting of **45** would probably give beginners the most trouble from this group. Quite a few finales are rigidly entrenched — 1. ... S~ 2. Q(x)d4, 1. ... Kd6 2. Qc5, and 1. ... Kf6 2. Qg7. An unresolved 1. ... Ke4! steers the search to 1. Bf2. 2. Qe3 then invests that bugbear, as well as the proffered 1. ... Kxf4.

46. RAL
Original

#2

47. N SIOTIS
The Problemist,
1980

#2

48. R A LINCOLN
The Problemist,
1999

#2

49. O STOCCHI
Magyar Sakkvilág,
1933

#2 (Version by RAL)

50. R A LINCOLN
StrateGems,
1999

#2

51. R A LINCOLN
Newark Star-Ledger,
1987

#2

52. V MELNICHENKO
Smena,
1994

#2

53. PROF. K MLYNKA
Práca,
1993

#2

54. G MOTT-SMITH
Chess Review,
1937

#2

BELFORT

Stipulations for composing tourneys enter into strange *recherché* realms. The 1994 F.I.D.E. meeting at Belfort, France asked for tries of 1. Qe1? and 1. Qc2? while mandating 1. Qa4! as key. These were alternatives played by Anatoly Karpov versus Garry Kasparov during their highly theoretical Grünfeld debate. The latter was best, earning a brilliancy prize in the 1988 Belfort World Cup. **46** is the only imperfect reduction I could fashion. 1. ... Bg3! nixes 1. Qe1? (2. Qh4). 1. ... Bf5! disrupts 1. Qc2? (2. Qg6,Qh7). The far-flung 1. Qa4! (2. Qe8) eagerly hurtles across board 2. Qh4 for 1. ... Bf5.

BIKOS THEME

The Bikos theme describes reciprocal change between defensive functions. **47** has a lucid exposition. The "mistake" of 1. ... Be3 2. Qxe3 is unguard and 1. ... Be4 self-blocks for 2. Qh5. The roles flip-flop when 1. Sc3 brandishes (2. Qe2). 1. ... Be3 (2. Qh5) becomes self-block and 1. ... Be4 (2. Qxe4) transmutes to unguard.

My **48** capitalizes on similar tactics. 1. ... Se4 2. Qxe4 and 1. ... Bf4 2. Qd1 are primed. Inversion follows a try, 1. Se6? (2. Sg5), *i.e.* 1. ... Se4 2. Qd1 and 1. ... Bf4 2. Qxf4. But 1. ... Sh7! secures. Another knight poke, 1. Sd3! (2. Se1), fares better. Black dockings on e4 or f4 bisect the queen's line to g4. However, comebacks cognate with the try resurface.

The Bikos ideal can be conveyed in zugzwang format. The renowned Italian problemist Octavio Stocchi was first to herald the widely imitated structure of **49.** Initial conditions knock off 1. ... Sf~ 2. Q(x)d5, 1. ... Sc7 2. Qxc7 (unguard), and 1. ... Sb6 2. Rc7 (self-block correction). Not 2. Qc7? because b5 would hang. 1. Qd4 slues 1. ... Sb6 to unguard for 2. Qxb6. 1. ... Sc7 becomes the self-block correction requiring 2. Rb6 as 2. Qb6? leaves d7 exposed.

50 is another Bikos waiter. 1. Qc5? barrels in to bullyrag Black's rook. 2. Q(x)d6 is on ice if he tootles about aimlessly. 1. ... Rd7 "corrects" with self-block for 2. Re5, but 1. ... Rxd5! survives. 1. Qb5! flaunts 2. Q(x)d7 at desultory rook moves and the correction self-block changes to 1. ... Rd6 2. Re5. Now 2. Qe8 convincingly flusters 1. ... Rxd5. A set 1. ... Ke7 2. Qe1 drifts to 2. Qe2.

BLACK PAWN SHOP

The slow trudge of defending pawns earmarks them convenient dupes for the composer's wishes. Novel uses continue to be fabricated. It seems incredible that possibilities have not dried up. Coupled companions in **51** restrain ugly queen approaches to c6 or f6. 1. Qh3 (2. Qxd7) coaxes 1. ... d6 2. Qb3 and 1. ... e6 2. Qd3. 1. ... Kd6 is forestalled 2. Rd4. 1. ... e5 obligingly serves to validate White's threat.

52 has a self-block 1. ... bxa4 accede to 2. Rd5. 1. Ra3? deals with 1. ... b4 2. Re5 but makes 1. ... bxa4! scot-free. 1. axb5! transfers 2. Rd5 to slap 1. ... Kxb5. A brand new self-block, 1. ... axb5, reprises the erstwhile try 2. Ra3.

53 erects a battery, 1. Rh5, proposing 2. Sb6 to hinder forward progress of the b7 footman. 2. Sb4 confounds 1. ... Kb5 (not 2. Se7? Kb4!). The barricade 1. ... b5 clogs the duct for 2. Bb4. Here's a close conceptual relative with # 35. When defensive efforts go to b5, each mating punch alights on b4.

The "one-two" step of given infantry meets sundry and glorious applications. A nice retreating 1. Sb2 commences **54.** Auxiliary guard on c4 proves decisive. 1. ... c6 and 1. ... c5 fence off prospective shelters to permit 2. Qf5 and 2. Qg2 in succession. 1. ... d3 opens the queen's "look" at e4 after 2. Qc4.

55. C PATZKE
Freie Presse,
1993

#2

56. W SUESMAN
Providence Journal,
1947

#2

57. T TIKKANEN
The Problemist,
1984

#2

58. RAL
Original

#2 (b) Kg8>f2

59. M MARANDYUK
1st Prize, *Smena,*
1993

#2

60. H J DRAPER
The Problemist,
1987

#2

61. L GROLMAN
Smena,
1997

#2

62. RAL
Original

#2

63. V ANTIPOV
Kudesnik,
1997

#2

BLACK PAWN SHOP (CONT'D)

Black's king enjoys uncontaminated escape hatches in **55**. White embarks a sparkling 1. Qd7 (2. Qxb5) putting rook at risk *ad interim*. Immediate gratification is expressly polluted 1. ... Kxc5 2. Qd4. The a-pawn marches off with these perils — 1. ... a6 2. Qc7 and 1. ... a5 2. Rc6.

One block, (1. ... d6 2. Qf5), is already pronounced in **56**. 1. Sa6 posits (2. Sc7) which is still fatal should 1. ... Kd5 take wing. That outlet is blinded by 1. ... d5 whence 2. Sc5 asserts sway on d7.

How can White prohibit the enemy's unfettered f4 freedom in **57**? A magnificent solution, 1. Sh2, bestows two additional canals. Now 1. ... Kf4 decamps upon pain of 2. Qe5. The audacious chevalier crusades *de novo* to catch 1. ... Kh5 2. Sf3. 2. Qf6 prowls for 1. ... h5 and 2. Qg4 wrecks 1. ... h6 (or 1. ... Kh4). Sadly, this miniature was published a year prior to the untimely death of Finnish composer Tapani Tikkanen.

The twinned **58** has White's majesty intrude from different directions to usurp vital territory. 1. ... Kc6 is glibly slain 2. Se7, but that c-pawn cedes nothing. The first phase has 1. Kf7 support the bishop's exertions in obtaining 2. Be6 for a self-block 1. ... c6, and 2. Bb7 for an open gate 1. ... c5. Part (b) sees 1. Ke3 abet visits by the throne mate. 1. ... c6 and 1. ... c5 are sandbagged with 2. Qd4 and 2. Qe4.

59 shows the modern appetence for tries at any price. 1. Sf5? speculates on 1. ... d6 2. Sd4 or 1. ... d5 2. Qe7, but 1. ... Kd5! 1. Rc5! amends mates for 1. ... d6 2. f5 and 1. ... d5 2. Rc6 (set 2. Rh6). Of course, 2. Qe5 conks 1. ... Kd6. For me, refutations merely taking a flight are less than creative. Yet this layout was nonetheless deemed a prize winner.

Neoteric ways of handling Black pawn promotions go on apace. I think the following brace exude a fresh whiff of originality. **60** has a latent pin mate 2. Rf1 discouraging 1. ... Kd1. 1. Rf2 jinxes the pawn to admit masked bishop protection on d1. Attendant rebirths of queen or knight cultivate the expected dichotomy by 1. ... e1=Q 2. Rc2 and 1. ... e1=S 2. Bb2. Most schemes of this nature educe their value from "dual avoidance. " The queen and knight work ideally for such goals. That is why conversions to bishop or rook are generally not recorded within the rota of thematic participants.

A more innovative project embraces four promotions. They are very carefully calculated to separate impending duals. **61** also starts with a rook ambushing the adversarial target 1. Rh2. 1. ... e1=Q and 1. ... exd1=S repel 2. Qb2? affording solely 2. Rc2. The cute corresponding pair is 1. ... e1=S and 1. ... exd1=Q, which scrupulously avert 2. Rc2? to insist on 2. Qb2.

White's cavalry are poised to jump on two self-blocks in **62** — 1. ... c5 2. Sc3 and 1. ... e5 2. Se7. A laggard 1. ... c6! behooves careful thought. So the royal sovereign graciously steps aside 1. Ke3 where he is commuted by his consort 2. Qd3.

One doleful pawn can be contorted to accrue three self-blocks as **63** amply shows. The trio of choices are blanketed 1. ... d6 2. Bb6, 1. ... d5 2. Qc2, and 1. ... dxc6 2. Qd4. No adequate stalling gesture beckons except 1. Bb8 to supplant a proxy 2. Ba7 for 1. ... d6. There may be but few avenues of attaining the desired object in this manner. Unfortunately, the trenchant opinion of experts would never smile approvingly on such an innocent bagatelle.

64. RAL
Original

#2

65. F LINDGREN
Aftonbladet,
1927

#2

66. R J BERMUDEZ
Chess Review,
1937

#2

67. R ZEPLER
L'Echecs Marseillas,
1925

#2

68. A HILDEBRAND
3rd Prize, Chepizhny JT,
1994

#2

69. R A LINCOLN
Smena,
1996

#2

70. B GENKIN
Chess Life & Review,
1979

#2

71. R A LINCOLN
The Problemist,
1995

#2

72. J HARING
Sozavox,
1987

#2

BLACK PAWN SHOP (CONT'D)

A comparable arrangement in **64** also harvests a trifecta from the d-pawn. 1. Bb6 tarries by annexing more custody over c7. The "one-two" advances self-block in routine manner 1. ... d6 2. Qb5 and 1. ... d5 2. Qc7. 1. ... dxe6 is a self-injury which 2. Qxe6 consumes. Finally, 1. ... S~ submits to 2. Q(x)c5. Queen jolts arrive left, right, over, and under the doomed king.

A single Black pawn can engender four disparate replies. This maximum aftermath has been tagged "Pickaninny." Lindgren's **65** is at once economical and refined. It endures as a unique *pièce de résistance* among miniatures. 1. Qe2 menaces a mate on e7 which 1. ... exd6 permits. 1. ... exf6 diverts to 2. Qe8 while 1. ... e6 jams that square giving 2. Qb5. At length, 1. ... e5 leaves the front door ajar where 2. Qg4 rushes in. Such a classic realization cannot be bettered.

BLACK PRINCIPALS

The following assembly concentrates on activity of certain Black defenders. A sole bishop is star entertainer in nine exhibitions. **66** is the earliest version I could locate of what seems an age-old ruse. 1. Bd1 (2. Qd4) poisons the king breakaway 1. ... Kc4 2. Qb3. The isolated prelate's offers of assistance recoil with self-blocks 1. ... Bc3 2. Qe2 and 1. ... Be3 2. Qc2.

All bases are covered in **67**. 1. ... B~ empowers 2. Qf4 and 1. ... Kf3 saunters into 2. Qg3. But White cannot freely waste a tempo. The belligerent 1. Qe5? (2. Qxe4) detaches 1. ... d5! 1. Rc4! adopts 2. Qg3 against 1. ... B~Northeast, while dedicating 2. Qa3 for 1. ... B~Northwest. Note that 1. Ra4?, with like motivation, falters to an alert 1. ... Bd5!, fighting off 2. Qa3?

A useful "focal point" image arises in **68**. 1. Kh8 paradoxically self-pins the g-pawn to be loosened 1. ... B~Northwest 2. g8=S. B~Southwest (or 1. ... Bg5) are trounced 2. Q(x)g5 and 1. ... Bxg7 happily quaffs 1. ... Bxg7+.

69 engineers an aptly liberal 1. Be4 to the sequestered churchman's chagrin. 1. ... B~ forfeits 2. Q(x)e7 and 1. ... Bxd6 is debilitated by 2. Bd5. There's no reprieve coming through either 1. ... Kxd6 2. Qf6 or 1. ... Kf7 2. Qg6.

One would assuredly be inclined to keep 1. ... Kxg6 2. Qg8 undisturbed for **70**. The other flight capture 1. ... Kxg4 has White cash in 2. Qg2. The main question lingers on how to throttle the side-board ecclesiastic. An exhilarating dive, 1. Qh1 (2. Qxh5), hauls self-blocks over the coals — 1. ... Bxg6 2. Qh4 and 1. ... Bxg4 2. Qh6. The threat works perfectly fine following 1. ... Kxg6. This pleasing delicacy makes each Black move a capture.

71 diffuses several bogus detours. 1. Qe3? (2. Qh3) gets blunted 1. ... Bxg2! The sly 1. Bf3?, envisions 1. ... B~ 2. g4 and 1. ... Bxg2 2. Bxg2, but gets torn by 1. ... Be2! 1. Qd5? (2. Qh5) has 1. ... Bxg2 2. Qxg2 but is equally unavailing against the recurrent 1. ... Be2! Ironically, an implausible retreat, 1. Qc1!, chucks two different modes of lethal peekaboo at the pesky scoundrel — 1. ... B~ 2. B(x)e2 and 1. ... Bxg2 2. Bf3.

A gargantuan White phalanx assaults the meek bishop of **72**. That 1. ... Kh1 cranny is quarantined with a pin mate, 2. Qh8. Also, two overt battery salvoes are unambiguous. A 2. Rf3 cross-check greets 1. ... Bg2+ and 1. ... Bh3 conduces 2. Rgg1. 1. Qf4 forbids 1. ... B~Northwest by 2. Qf2 and the set for 1. ... Kh1 changes to 2. Qh6.

73. M LESCHEMELLE
Phénix,
1997

#2

74. V MELNICHENKO
Lokker MT,
1987

#2

75. N ZINOVYEV
1st Prize, *Smena,*
1989

#2

76. R T LEWIS
3rd Prize, *Buletin
problemistic,* 1987

#2

77. V KOZHAKIN
Segodiya zavtra,
1998

#2

78. RAL
Original

#2

79. R A LINCOLN
Newark Star-Ledger,
1999

#2

80. G MALEIKA
Deutsche Schachzeitung,
1980

#2

81. A KEIV
Smena,
1998

#2

BLACK PRINCIPALS (CONT'D)

White also fields a monster squad in **73.** The suave bishop is unabashed by two deficient incursions. 1. Bc6? sacks 1. ... Kd8 2. Qd7 and 1. ... Kd6 2. Qe5, but 1. ... Bf7! 1. Qd5? boasts 1. ... Kf6 2. Qe5, but 1. ... Bd7! 1. Qc8! scores with 2. Sf5 chasing 1. ... Kd6. 1. ... B~ (or 1. ... Kf6) are rebutted 2. Qe6. Quondam defenses can "correct" with familiar corollaries — 1. ... Bf7 2. Qd8 and 1. ... Bd7 2. Qf8.

After this mixed bag of "waiters," an authentic threat materializes in the grand **74.** I count it among personal favorites. 1. S~? evokes (2. Qg4). However, that vigilant bishop shears the newly opened line 1. ... Bg3! The daredevil warrior cracks the enigma 1. Se4! disabling any g4 checkmate while subrogating 2. Sg5. 1. ... Kh4 tramps into 2. Qh8 and 1. ... Bd2 resigns to 2. Sf2. The concluding caper 1. ... Bh4 2. Qd7 is unalloyed gold.

The next section retails five examples spotlighting Black queen. Her robust capacity makes buffering the White king from check a grave concern. **75** needs four placements to tame the b7 beast. An optimistic 1. Qg4? (2. Qg8) hopes for 1. ... Qxf7, 2. Qc8 or 1. ... Qg2 2. Qe6, but 1. ... Qe7! A wiser 1. Qg5! (2. Qg8) has 2. Qd8 coping with 1. ... Qxf7 and 2. Qxe7 devours 1. ... Qe7.

A large raft of tries gingers up **76.** 1. ... Q~ 2. Qxg5, 1. ... Qxg6 2. Qh3, and 1. ... Kh4 2. Rxh6 seem guaranteed. The dilemma is to conserve existing mates or find surrogates. Each White piece takes a bite at the coconut. 1. Rf6? (2. Qh3) is spoiled 1. ... Qxf6! 1. Qe6? (2. Rxh6) has 2. Qxg4 for 1. ... g4, but 1. ... Q~! 1. h3? alters 1. ... Kh4 to 2. Qg4, but 1. ... Qxg6! King "pauses" are laden with danger. The sixth rank is definitely off-limits — 1. ... Qxg6+! That retort also ruptures 1. Ke4? Dark squares of c5, e5, and d4 are restricted by checks. Only 1. Kc4! circumvents all queen havoc.

77 cajoles the lounging lady into four concessions. A forthright 1. Sc3 (2. Sb1) joyously revels due to 1. ... Qb6, 2. Qxa4, 1. ... Qb5 2. Sxb5, 1. ... Qb4 2. Qa2, and 1. ... Qxc3+2. Qxc3. Such a series of diversified mates is not easy to obtain. Tiptop solid construction fulfills those fortuitous circumstances where no duals rear their vile head.

Those pawns in **78** form an aegis to keep White's king unmolested. They also acquire jobs as try spoilers. Where (2. Qc7) is the constant threat, 1. ... axb6! mocks 1. Bb6? and 1. ... b6! daunts 1. Ba5? 1. Bb8? has the regent wade into action 1. ... Qe5! Proper is 1. Bd6! instigating Black queen byplay 1. ... Qg7 2. Qe8 and 1. ... Qd8 2. Qxb7.

Lesser officers arduously subjugate her royal highness in **79.** 1. Rf4 (2. Sf2) creeps toward the dread impaler who thrashes wildly 1. ... Qxf4+ 2. Sxf4 and 1. ... Qc5 2. Rf3. Keys by pinned pieces figure rarely in miniatures.

The next quartet contains Black rook exercises. Amazingly enough, **80** stockpiles seven virtual or actual wind-ups. The furtive 1. Qe2 builds a short-stepping battery to dominate a roistering castle. Set replies for 1. ... Rxf3 2. Qh4 and 1. ... Rxf5 2. Qg4 are relayed to 2. Qxf3 and 2. Qh2. That frisky rapscallion fills the dance card with 1. ... R~ 2. f4, 1. ... Re4 2. fxe4, 1. ... Rg4 2. fxg4, and 1. ... Rh4 2. Sg3.

White's bishop of **81** will streak off to augur (2. Qb2). This much is plain as a pikestaff. 1. Ba3? is opposed 1. ... Rb1! and 1. ... Rxc1! chomps 1. Bc1? A corner plunge 1. Ba1! shines, where self-blocks produce 1. ... Rb1 2. Qa4 and 1. ... Rxa1 2. Qb3. This modest regimen has wholesome unity. Beginners can be rewarded when investigating those alluring false leads.

82. J RICE
Chess Problems for Solving,
1995

#2

83. RAL
Original

#2

84. W E LESTER
Chess Amateur,
1924

#2

85. S ISMILE
The Problemist,
1992

#2

86. L SZILAGYI
Il due mosse,
1960

#2

87. RAL
Original

#2

88. RAL
Original

#2

89. J RICE
Chess Problems for Solving,
1995

#2

90. MRS W J BAIRD
Chess Amateur,
1920

#2

BLACK PRINCIPALS (CONT'D)

82 finagles a swindle to waylay that eighth rank rook. The stout yeoman has 1. ... Rxd7! to repudiate such inroads as 1. Qe5? (2. Qc7, Qb8). 1. Qe6! makes any sanctuary evaporate suddenly. 1. ... Rxd7 self-pins for g-pawn coronation 2. g8=Q. Two more capture promotions occur if the woeful rook roves across to f8 or h8. Finally, 2. Qxe8 and 2. Qxg8 grab off leftover destinations. That a5 idler plugs an odious cook 1. Qa4 (2. Qa6,Qa8).

83 nearly replicates Rice's position with the d8 rook getting fed into a pervasive meat grinder. No decent tries emanate, so White hurriedly applies the indicated quietus, 1. g7. Four promotions plus the rook hit on c8 round out the transparent, but dual-free mating inventory.

Six problems complete the chapter by examining Black knights. Two rooks tangle with a tough customer in **84.** The initial position betrays a "total block. " Here is an amusing Mexican stand-off. Black's knight holds vigil over first rank checks but cannot quit his vantage point. White's bookends also cannot budge, *e.g.* 1. Rh2? Sf2! 1. Rge2! is good despite theft of the e1 portico. 1. ... S~ is thumped 2. Ra1 with a rectifying 1. ... Sc1 2. Rad2.

White can choose from 2. Q(x)e5, 2. Qd7, or 2. Bf7 to clobber knight departure in **85.** 1. Qc5? loiters where an ameliorative 1. ... Sxd4! is perceived. The shallow lunge, 1. Qd3!, fastens 2. Qe4 upon 1. ... S~. A better 1. ... Se5 allows 2. d5 giving mate on a flight square — an extraordinary phenomenon. 1. ... Kd5 is an onimous quaigmire — 2. Bf7.

86 is a fair technical drill, but has no puzzle value. Conspicuous parole from stalemate by 1. Re4 springs the distressed knight to be ravaged wherever he goes.

One solo gladiator again dictates four differentiated mates in **87.** A truly horrid key 1. Sxd7, broaching double "longshots" (2. Qa1, Qh1), sets the machine in motion. They are allocated singly after 1. ... Sd6 (only 2. Qa1) and 1. ... Sg7 (only 2. Qh1). Both targets are begrudged by 1. ... Sf6 or 1. ... Sc7 activating 2. Bxf6 and 2. Bxc7.

White has partial control over that knight duo in **88** — 1. ... Sc~ 2. Q(x)b4 and 1. ... Sd~ 2. b3. Annoying cankers are 1. ... Sb3! or 1. ... Sb5! 1. b4 modifies the tableau entirely. 1. ... Sc~ now imparts 2. Q(x)a5 while 2. Qxb4 returns to smite a "corrective" 1. ... Sxb4. The other knight commits a general error 1. ... Sd~ 2. Qxc6 patched by 1. ... Sb5 2. Qc2.

Both antagonists are under surveillance in **89.** 1. ... Sf~ Q(x)f7 confers 2. Q(x)g7 and 1. ... Sd~ sparks 2. Qf7 or 1. ... Sxe8 2. Qxe8. Two feeble attempts to hold the fort are 1. Kd8? Sb7+! and 1. Qh7? Sxe8! A threat, 1. f7! (2. Qg8), works when new possibilities adhere to 1. ... Sh6 2. Qxh6 and 1. ... Sg7 2. Qxd6. This neat problem serves as a bridge to the next category.

BLOCK AND TACKLE

Veteran problem sleuths are generally suspicious when each Black move meets resolution at the outset. One's normal reaction is to whiffle-waffle maintaining the situation, or some clever adjustment generating changed play. The notion of finding a threat is not foremost. That is why the "block threat" can often be a demon to unravel. **90** typically adverts plain sailing for 1. ... B~ 2. Q(x)c7 and 1. ... e5 2. Qb6 (or 2. Qd5). But feasible waiting moves are scarce as hen's teeth. So an abrupt 1. Qc3 (2. Qd4) changes 1. ... e5 to 2. Qc6.

91. A TRILLING
Magyar Sakkvilág,
1933

#2

92. R A LINCOLN
The Problemist,
1996

#2

93. A OLENIK
Priokkskaya pravda,
1989

#2

94. R A LINCOLN
The Problemist Supplement,
1999

#2

95. E WOLF
Magyar Sakkvilág,
1932

#2

96. V SHILNIKOV
Luninietskie naviny,
1994

#2 (b) Pc6>c7

97. J RICE
Chess Problems for Solving,
1995

#2

98. T KARDOS
Schach aktuell,
1981

#2

99. V SEVASTYANOV
Chernovy girnik,
1971

#2

Block and Tackle (cont'd)

Solvers would undoubtedly surmise **91** is a block threat right off the bat. White's queen cannot prolong her observation over 1. ... g6 2. Qxh6 and 1. ... d6 2. Qc8. Endeavors to willy-nilly reach the eighth rank are foiled by 1. Qh2? (2. Qb8) d6! and 1. Qh1? (2. Qa8) d5! 1. Qc3! plumps for (2. Qc8) bypassing d-pawn's ambit. The mellow bishop can now farm out one casual dollop, 1. ... Bxg5 2. Qxg7.

2. Qe7 proscribes Black knight moves in **92**. Restrictions on any White wiggle are as tight as a drum. But the bounteous 1. e5 (2. Qc4) foists that adverse charger into yet another pickle. 1. ... S~ bends to 2. Qf7 and a superior palliative 1. ... Sxe5 blocks for 2. Sf4.

93 has four set replies govern a spare contingent — 1. ... Bb3 2. Sxb3, 1. ... Bc2 2. Qxc2, 1. ... Bd1 2. Qe3, and 1. ... S~ 2. S(x)e2. No waiters present themselves, so 1. Sf3 takes a flyer at (2. Qd2). Only one refurbished mate appears with 1. ... Sb1 2. Qxb1. The bishop becomes a superfluous bystander.

White's absorbed queen watches over 1. ... c1=Q+ 2. Qxc1 and 1. ... S~ 2. Q(x)f2 in **94**. 1. Qxc2? strews a cluster of bottom row threats, but flops to 1. ... Sf2! A cautious 1. Kd3? gets brutally blasted 1. ... Sf4+! An ingenuous withdrawal, 1. Qc6!, peers at (2. Qg2). Those former defenses struggle with these catastrophes — 1. ... Sf4 2. Qh1 and 1. ... Sf2 2. Re1.

The compressed setting of **95** again has the White queen quite heavily engaged. 1. ... Sf~ delivers 2. Q(x)g5 and 2. Qxg6 quells 1. ... Sg6. A quick survey verifies there's no room to maneuver. 1. Rg3 pursues (2. Rf3) where 1. ... Sg6 shifts riposte to 2. Qxf7. 1. ... Sg5 complies with an unchanged 2. Qxg5 and a fretful reflex 1. ... Kf4 is hounded 2. Qg4.

Castles in the Air

Weaver Adams is fondly remembered for proclaiming the curiously improbable "White to play and win" mystique. He was a mildly eccentric but endearing pundit with penetrating chessic opinions. He once said: "Castling is a move, not a ceremony." Problemists, of course, hold castling in special reverence. Miniatures are a thriving arena for exploiting the special properties of this mere "move." Subdivisions within this segment have three positions dealing with the Black side and eight for White. **96** has an appreciable fusion of tries striving for (2. Rg8). 1. Kg6? discloses that Black's ultimate salvation resides in 1. ... 0-0-0! 1. Rc7? precludes that opportunity but Black scrapes up the chance 1. ... Kd8! 1. Ra7? goes seeking 1. ... 0-0-0 2. Ra8, but is foolish in light of 1. ... Rxa7! An unerring 1. Rb7! stays on the beam by surmounting 1. ... 0-0-0 2. Rgc7. (b) has a simplistic 1. Kg8 (2. Rf8).

97 escalates to a higher plane as White's key move clears the castling alley. 1. Sd5 (2. Qe7) tempts 1. ... 0-0-0, anxious to vault 2. Qb7. There are also non-castling defenses by king and rook which the busy queen gladly destroys — 1. ... Kd8 2. Qf8 and 1. ... Ra7 2. Qb8. That unused watchman on e5 legitimizes the castling option by "proving" Black could have had a previous play that did not entail king or rook.

98 flunks the retrograde analysis test. Some Black minion made a last move invalidating castling to either one side or the other. Regardless, this agenda was candidly ballyhooed by the composer: 1. Qc7? (2. Qe7) Kf8 2. Qf7, 1. ... 0-0 2. Qh7, 1. ... Ra7! 1. Qg7! (2. Qe7, Qxh8) Kd8 2. Qd7 and 1. ... 0-0-0 2. Qb7.

White castling is broadly suggested in **99**. 1. 0-0 supplies those guards to track 1. ... Kxc2 2. Qb1 and 1. ... Kxe4 2. Qf5.

100. R A LINCOLN
The Problemist,
1993

#2

101. D NADDOR
Chess Life,
1984

#2

102. J RICE
Kingston,
1997

#2

103. L KUBBEL
Kurortnaya Gazeta,
1939

#2

104. O WURZBURG
American Chess Bulletin,
1949

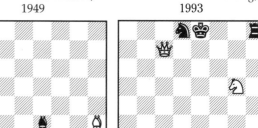

#2

105. K-P HOFFMAN
Neue Osnabrücker Zeitung,
1993

#2

106. F CHRISTIAANS
Neue Osnabrücker Zeitung,
1993

#2

107. K A K LARSEN
L'Echecs Marseillas,
1925

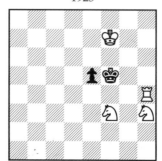

#2

108. RAL
Original

#2

CASTLES IN THE AIR (CONT'D)

Despite strenuous experimentation, I could not adapt a tolerable key to **100.** The ghastly compromise, 1. Qb7, caters nursemaid for that e4 huckleberry waving in the wind. However, there's a passable menu of four heterogeneous mates. Black is ineluctably shackled — 1. ... Bc2 2. Qd5, 1. ... Kc2 2. Qxb1, 1. ... c2 2. Ra3, and 1. ... Ba2 2. 0-0-0.

An utterly exquisite key initiates **101.** A benevolent 1. Sd3 has shrewd designs on (2. Sb4). 1. ... Kxd3 flounders into the main attraction 2. 0-0-0. Sideshows by the b5 spear carrier embellish grandly. Each knight gets erased in turn to provoke 1. ... Bxd3 2. Qa2 and 1. ... Bxa4 2. Qc4.

102 has another pawn-free framework for castling. This frolic edifice tantalizes unwary solvers with 1. 0-0? (2. Qc3) which receives a jarring wake up call 1. ... Rg5+! A nonchalant 1. Ke2! (2. Qc3) potently stifles all of the rook's guile — 1. ... Re5+ 2. Bxe5, 1. ... Ra3 2. Qxa3, and 1. ... Ra2+ 2. Bc2.

The top-drawer technician can make castling keys palatable. In this province, Soviet composer Leonid Kubbel was *sans pareil* as **103** richly demonstrates. 1. 0-0-0 (2. Sb1) plans to pinch the c3 recess where 1. ... a1=Q+ matters not a whit. That misfire (2. Se4?) would hamper the queen's gaze at e3. A droll turnabout comes through 1. ... Kc3 which insists on 2. Se4 and not 2. Sb1?

The king/rook combo can be wangled to transmit four mates. **104** assembles this minor miracle with relatively scant means. 1. Rf2 sidles over putting the question to a frantic bishop. B~Northeast (or 1. ... Kg1) are rudely accosted 2. Rf1. 1. ... Bxf2+ or 1. ... Bd2+ suffer patent revenge by 2. Kxf2 and 2. Kxd2. 1. ... B~Northwest allows 2. Ke2 or 2. Kd2 and 1. ... Bd4 induces 2. 0-0-0.

Castling by both sides can transpire without strain in bigger positions. But it is difficult to imagine a miniature model. Given a charitable mood, no aesthetic sensibilities would be offended by the outré **105.** A purist might take grievous exception to the unprovided 1. ... Rh1+! 1. 0-0-0 (2. Qxd8, Rxd8) poaches on the castled preserve by 2. Qh7 after 1. ... 0-0. Knight retreats are coarsely manhandled 2. Q(x)f7.

Imitation has been attributed as the sincerest form of flattery. **106** appeared in the same pages a few month's later. Wholesale renovations have White kingside castling launched against an opponent seeking safety through his queen-side counterpart. The disagreeable 1. ... Ra1+! again violates canons of acceptability. 1. 0-0 espies (2. Qf8, Rf8) with the "castled" rook applying the coup 2. Rc1 for 1. ... 0-0-0. An abortive 1. ... Se7 is swept off 2. Qxe7.

CHANGING PARTNERS

Fifteen examples are presented which illustrate the various shades of "mutate." This standard device is adored among solvers and composers alike. It is characterized by a starting premise of total block which cannot be maintained. At least one changed mate always occurs. **107** is a elementary setup. 2. Rf4 checks 1. ... e4 but White is understandably stuck for a move. 1. Sh2 affably drops to guard g4 where 1. ... e4 now gives 2. Rh5.

108 packages the motif with barest of extremes. 1. ... e5 2. Qc4 is easy as pie but must be jettisoned. 1. Sc5 displaces 1. ... e5 to then trigger a qualitatively preferred ideal mate 2. Qd2.

109. W SPECKMANN
The Problemist,
1986

#2

110. DR T LASLO
Magyar Sakkvilág,
1931

#2

111. S BOROS & F LAZARD
Magyar Sakkvilág,
1926

#2

112. L TALABÉR
Feladványkedvelök Lapja,
1971

#2

113. R TIKLER & Z ZILAHI
Magyar Sakkvilág,
1926

#2

114. V MELNICHENKO
The Problemist,
1988

#2

115. E SZENTGYÖRGI
Magyar Sakkvilág,
1928

#2

116. R T LEWIS
The Problemist,
1983

#2

117. R TAUBER
*Schweizeische
Schachzeitung,* 1924

#2

CHANGING PARTNERS (CONT'D)

Every set mate does not necessarily get replaced in the average mutate. **109** has White keep his f5 whammer trained on 1. ... S~ 2. B(x)g4 unceasingly. That bustling bishop is also responsible for 1. ... f6 2. Bg6. A feigned evacuation. 1. Bd7. continues vigilance over g4 while slipping into a rear entrance 2. Be8 after pawn moves.

110 has the Black king's pitifully lonesome subaltern slated for 1. ... B~ 2. Qb5 and 1. ... Bc5 2. Qd3. White's own bishop would be happy to squander a tempo. but is curbed by the f7 "plug." 1. Qh5 politely retires from the scene to mete out a more visually enticing 2. Qxf7 for 1. ... Bc5.

Fledgling solvers could be pleased as Punch with the blithe antics of **111**. 1. ... S~ 2. Q(x)d4 is untenable for a permanent basis so 1. Sd2 reroutes 2. Q(x)d6 against knight digressions. Shifting hits from below to above the bull's eye has gratifying allure. Not to be forgotten is the bonus mate 1. ... Ke5 2. Qe4.

112 is also identified as "one change-one added." An intimidated Black king is beset by a bevy of swarming troopers. 1. ... Kc5 2. Sc6 is a piece of cake about to go stale. As usual, nothing can foster the status quo. An electrifying scoot, 1.Qh6, supercharges the lady to return with a vengeance. 2. Qb6 now attends 1. ... Kc5 and the gratuitous e5 "gift" is obviously corrupted 1. ... Kxe5 2. Qd6.

Cursory inspection of **113** ascertains another mutate in the offing. 2. Qd4 chaperones that fugitive 1. ... Ke4, but White cannot laze away a move. 1. Qc7 delectably swerves to refocus 2. Qe5 on 1. ... Ke4. A secondary participant avidly envelops the collateral hidey-hole after 1. ... Ke6 2. Bc4.

Viktor Melnichenko excels among the supreme miniaturists of our era. His prolific argosy is not diminished by anything second-rate. Ordinary mortals often labor through fallow periods when ideas refuse to gel. But this specialist habitually gets those stubborn pieces to cooperate. **114** is an irresistible mutate where White must involuntarily abandon 1. ... f4 2. Qh3. 1. Qe5 finds more fertile pastures to whack 1. ... f4 by 2. Qg5. Generally, quid pro quo of self-block for strategically inferior open gate is poor business. However, Black got a royal parking spot gratis. As supposed, that fleeting freedom is cruelly repossessed 1. ... Kh4 2. Qf4.

115 looks deceptively elementary. 2. Rf5 bops 1. ... S~ and that's that. Still, no trifling squirm sustains this outcome. White's king is compelled to keep his distance from the marauding knight. 1. Qe2 offers g3 so to gash 1. ... S~ with 2. Q(x)f3. The newly gained alcove is forbidden because 1. ... Kg3 2. Qh2.

A hasty peep at **116** spurs a twinge of déjà vu. Isn't this Szentgyörgi's problem? Well — no. Having White's king bear on g6 reaps a radically altered improvement. The fabulous try, 1.Rh5?, garners 1. ... S~ 2. g6 where 2. Sd4 bruises the "correcting" 1. ... Sf4. But the astute 1. ... Se5! dodges White's grasp. 1. Qe3! carries out the schedule as witnessed previously.

There are cases where a particular set mate gets plural replacement. **117** has 1. ... Sc~ squelched 2. Q(x)d5 and 1. ... Se~ by 2. Q(x)f4. 1. Qh5 leaves the d5 clout untouched. Now 1. ... Se~ brings 2. Qg4 and 1. ... Sf4 2. Sc5. The post-key play integrates more auspicious tactics with loss of line control plus correction over a meager unguard.

118. N IVANOVSKY
Mat,
1969

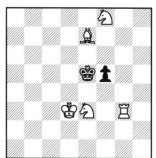

#2

119. R ASPLUND
Tidskrift för Schack,
1958

#2

120. F J KOVACS
Falkirk Herald,
1923

#2

121. R T LEWIS
The Problemist,
1980

#2

122. S LOYD
American Chess Nuts,
1868

#2

123. R A LINCOLN
Newark Star-Ledger,
1996

#2

124. A MARKEVITCH
Comm., *StrateGems,*
1998

#2

125. J GREEN
StrateGems,
1999

#2

126. R A LINCOLN
Kudesnik,
1998

#2

Changing Partners (cont'd)

The last four selections have two changes from set to actual. This exigent program taxes skills of composers to the nth degree. Mutates of this kind are only encountered sporadically. **118** succeeds without commissioning a White queen. Initial diagram has Black taking a flier 1. ... Kf4 2. Bd6, then stuffing that egress 1. ... f4 2. Rg5. Everything is glued *in situ* except 1. Rh3 enacting 1. ... Kf4 2. Sg6 and 1. ... f4 2. Rh5. The first substitution is admirable by hiring a standby assassin. Conversely, the other pales as mediocre "concurrent" mate.

Asplund's congregation is crammed toward the left border in **119.** This practical apparatus dilutes White's prerogatives. Solvers will have to doctor up new remedies for 1. ... b4 2. Qd3 and 1. ... bxa4 2. Rxc5. 1. Qb2 is the artful swirl with revisions 1. ... b4 2. Qc2 (still self-block) and 1. ... bxa4 2. Rxa4 (self-injury instead of open gate).

In **120,** White would be ecstatic to dawdle for the prosaic 1. ... Se~ 2. Q(x)g4 and 1. ... Sf~ 2. Q(x)h6. 1. Sf3 adroitly switches rebuttals to 1. ... Se~ 2. Qxf5 and 1. ... Sf~ 2. Q(x)h4.

I deem **121** as the finest miniature mutate on record. Tony Lewis is one of Great Britain's preeminent problemists. He has explored the frontiers of changed play in a plethora of superlative creations. Here, each member of White's squadron concocts a truly reasonable attempt to outwit that wily foe. Cut and dried sets are 1. ... g6 2. Bg6, 1. ... g5 2. Qf7, and 1. ... S~ 2. Q(x)e5. 1. Ke3? would insert 2. R(x)f4 for 1. ... S~, but 1. ... g5! 1. Re4? gets nonplused 1. ... Sf4! 1. Bh5? tumbles to 1. ... g6! 1. Qd6? (2. Qg6) lets the quarry flee 1. ... Kg5! With a murmur of relief, 1. Bf7! solves. New mates are 1. ... g6 2. Be6 and 1. ... g5 2. Qe6.

Charity Cases

The next seven positions have only one thing in common. They grant "gift" flights to the Black king. Experts descry such hocus-pocus in a jiffy, but beginners are frequently gulled and titillated by these prodigal gambits. The caprice of marooning a White rook was probably already hackneyed by 1868. Nevertheless, **122** still holds up today as a propitious citation of sacrificial key. 1. Re3 comes as a bolt from the blue. Variations are 1. ... S~ 2. Q(x)e5, 1. ... g3 2. Re4, and 1. ... Kxe3 2. Qd2.

123 puts e6 on the plate to combat an imminent pawn "one-two. " The gentle sideslip 1. Qf4 proficiently shellacks 1. ... e6 2. Qd6, 1. ... e5 2. Qc4, 1. ... S~ 2. Q(x)e4, and 1. ... Ke6 2. Qf5.

White's aloof queen must relocate to a profitable perspective in **124.** 1. Qa2 dogs the renegade king implacably — 1. ... Ke5 2. Qd5 and 1. ... Ke3 2. Qa7. 1. ... Kxc3 accepts the Trojan horse to get enfolded by a bewildering ideal mate 1. Qa1. A hardworking peripheral rook patrols six squares.

Joshua Green made his two-mover miniature debut with the sterling **125.** 1. Sh2 briskly absconds to skulk in wait for 1. ... Ke5 2. Sf3 and 1. ... Ke3 2. Sf5. That double-barreled windfall is a rosy harbinger of blooming talent.

126 conscripts an identical lineup of performers. How does White discomfit that d7 drone? 1. Qc3 realigns parceling out temporary visas to d6 and e4. 1. ... d6 is promptly squeezed 2. Sf6 and 1. ... Kd6 gets apprehended 2. Qe5. 1. ... Ke4 2. Qc4 is a "model mirror" mate. Nothing lies adjacent upon the Black king's eight passageways and every unit (excluding pawns) is utilized. Furthermore, flights are guarded but once.

127. P BENKO
Chess Life,
1980

#2

128. RAL
Original

#2

129. F SACKMANN
*Deutsche Arbeiter
Schachzeitung, 1909*

#2

130. A HARTH
Chess Life & Review,
1974

#2

131. S INOSTROZA
The Problemist,
1986

#2

132. W SPECKMANN
Tidskrift för Schack,
1967

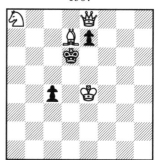

#2

133. RAL
Original

#2

134. P SHALIMOV
Leninskaya smena,
1983

#2

135. C MANSFIELD
The Tablet,
1955

#2

CHARITY CASES (CONT'D)

These last two items feature White largesse which conceals a threat. **127** has 1. Sd3 (2. Qd1) sally forth where 1. ... cxd3 blocks for 2. Sd4 and 1. ... Kxd3 strays to 2. Qb1. 2. Sd4 also lassoes the nomadic 1. ... Kb3.

In **128,** Black savors an untrammeled burrow, 1. ... Kf2. With this caveat, ceding another lodge would not be remiss. 1. Sf4 (2. Qh4) deftly contests 1. ... Kf2 2. Qe1, 1. ... Kxf4 2. Qh2, and 1. ... f2 2. Se2.

CLEARANCE SALE

Clearance devolves on a line-moving piece rambling off to some appointed destination. A comrade-in-arms then promenades along that same trajectory from behind. Hence, the lead-off man is not dodging to one side. As the date on **129** indicates, clearance has been a salutary gadget for ages. White foresees a consequent 2. Qe3 moorage after rook migrates westward. But 1. Rc3? isn't far enough since 1. ... Kf6! skedaddles away. 1. Ra3! provides elbow room for 2. Qc3 to lash that rogue. The itinerant rook buttresses 2. Qe3 for any Black descent to the fourth rank as planned.

There are occasions when a constituent becomes redundant. In **130,** 1. Ra1 emancipates the queen to stalk 1. ... Ke3 2. Qe1 and 1. ... Kf5 2. Qb1. The lead rook has no supporting role for these mates and might just as well have disappeared from the board.

The next two instances have a bishop harnessed as front runner with queen following in his wake. The 1. Ba1 swoop of **131** is abundantly insinuated with that jeopardized rook at stake. An amazon dame infiltrates three tunnels 1. ... Kxa2 2. Qb2, and 1. ... Kb4 (or 1. ... Kc4) 2. Qc3. A non-clearance mate 1. ... b4 2. Qg8 is best of the lot.

132 has the bishop plummet 1. Ba4 on a milk run expedition to inflict (2. Qc6). Refuge by 1. ... Kc5 is ravished 2. Qxe7. Moves by e-pawn vacate that square for potential access. But 1. ... e6 self-blocks granting 2. Qf8. What really sparkles is the self-injury 1. ... e5 which acts as Black line opening. White is tickled pink to polish off 2. Qxe5.

Most clearance schemes have the queen couched for trailing after weaker subordinate. **133** reverses the formula where a stronger team mate goes first. Worthwhile tries are mapped 1. Ra4? (2. Rxc4) Rc1! and 1. Ra3? R~ 2. Q(x)e3, but 1. ... Re2! 1. Qf2! facilitates rook's arrival 2. R(x)e2 against 1. ... R~. That plucky assistant gets an additional lick 1. ... c3 2. Ra4. Finally, her majesty short-circuits a residual culprit, 1. ... Re3 2. Qh4.

134 is a stunning technical achievement where one rook waltzes ahead for another. Only the faint-hearted would fret over the unprovided a7 hovel. 1. Rc7 plows ahead to bring 2. R2c6 in his train after Black "clears" 1. ... b5. Ancillary mates spill profusely — 1. ... a2 2. Rxa2, 1. ... b6 2. Qa4, and 1. ... Ka7 2. Qxb7.

COINCIDENCE

Anyone who has ventured into composition is haunted by a gnawing specter of anticipation. No matter how clever the artifice, there is a palpable risk that someone else did it before. Here are some amusing coincidences that occur when like-minded problemists latch onto the same idea. **135** has 1. ... B~Northeast 2. Sd6, and 1. ... B~Northwest 2. Sc3 set. 1. Rf3 swings the mates 1. ... B~Northeast 2. Sg3 and 1. ... B~Northwest 2. Sf6. The legendary Comins Mansfield was stung by anticipation on this knickknack. The same earlier saw light of day courtesy of Knut Arnstam, *Schachvärlden* 1943.

136. J POTTER
American Chess Nuts,
1868

#2

137. J SCHUMER
Transvaal Leader,
1906

#2

138. K FÖRSTER & R A LINCOLN
The Problemist, 1993

#2

139. G MOTT-SMITH
Chess Review,
1937

#2

140. C OUELLET & R A LINCOLN
The Problemist, 1993

#2

141. R A LINCOLN
Newark Star-Ledger,
1987

#2

142. G MOTT-SMITH
Chess Review,
1939

#2

143. J STEWART
Falkirk Herald,
1921

#2

144. RAL
Original

#2

COINCIDENCE (CONT'D)

Those positions with less than seven tenants are conventionally nicknamed "subminiatures." An immense bonanza of four men heirlooms can be unearthed in the literature. Here are two yeasty products from the annals of yore. **136** cannot allow 1. ... Ka7 to go unheeded. An ad hoc 1. Sc8 purveys the axiomatic give-and-take gewgaw to fetch 1. ... Kxc8 2. Qa8. Though nowise profound, any rational puzzle budding from such scrimpy fragments is still a substantial accomplishment.

Lo and behold, over forty years elapse and a near simulacrum blossoms. **137** ranges three of the minuscule gathering exactly so. Odd man out is bishop also assigned to crash on c8. This time 1. Bc8 embroils a (2. Qb7) noose toppling 1. ... Ka7. And of course, 1. ... Kxc8 again solicits 2. Qa8. Without increasing material, Schumer's tiny postscript ingeniously revamps a waiter into a threat problem.

Great Britain's John Rice is author of several books and issues a steady stream of instructive articles galore. As primary organizer of many events, he's become an assiduous impresario of the art. **138** took part in a tourney he directed for "White castlers." I did not collaborate with German composer Klaus Förster — we both sent this position! Our main objective concerned drubbing that Black 1. ... Kb2 shimmy through 2. Qa2. A prim offset, 1. Qe6, zooms 2. Qe2 upon 1. ... b3. 1. ... Kxd3 listlessly slouches into the expectant arms of 2. 0-0-0.

I was astonished to later come across **139** which smoothly surpasses that mild chimera. 1. Qe6 ushers in the same three variations. However, by forsaking that 1. ... Kb2 hutch initially, this grouping charts a prized fourth outcome 1. ... cxb2 2. Qc4.

Rice's castling competition attracted several entries signifying joint credit. Again, I thought up **140** independent of Canadian composer Charles Ouellet. This express layout couldn't be topped had we compared notes. Tries abound where an exuberant Black rider despoils every single foray. 1. Bc1? (2. Be3) Sd2! 1. Bb2? (2. Bd4) Sc3! 1. Sc2? (2. Bc5) Sxa3! 1. Sd3! (2. Bc5) prudently guards f2 so 1. ... Sxa3 will warrant 2. O-O-O.

141 was sculpted to contrast direct return captures versus enemy checks. White needs not fuss about 1. ... h4+ as 2. Qxh4 is a haymaker. After the screws tighten 1. Qf7 (2. Qxh5), 1. ... h4+ changes in deference to 2. Rxh4. 2. Qxg7 and 2. Qg6 bombard 1. ... R~ and 1. ... Kh6.

Geoffrey Mott-Smith was a faithful contributor of dozens of imaginative problems to *Chess Review* and *American Chess Bulletin* during the 1930s and 1940s. I blinked twice when regarding his **142.** This contains the same seven actors crunched together in suffocating proximity. His interpretation has 1. Qe5 suddenly steal away to hammer 1. ... h5+ 2. Qxh5, 1. ... R~ 2. Qxg7, 1. ... Kxf5 2. Qf5, and 1. ... Kh8 2. Rxh6. These tactics are also analogous to # 431.

143 is an unassuming mutate which replaces 1. ... f2 2. Qg2 with 2. Qxe4 after backing off 1. Qf4. The other electives, 1. ... e3 2. Qxf3 and 1. ... B~ 2. Q(x)h2, are present in the initial diagram.

My carbon copy **144** was designed while unaware of Stewart's forerunner. The equation appears indistinguishable after 1. Qf4. There's no attempt to breed a mutate. Instead, I propagated this frivolous ripple of tries which fizzle to each of the Black king's entourage — 1. Qd5? B~! 1. Qd1? f2! 1. Qe1? e3!

145. T HERLIN
Schachzeitung,
1852

#2

146. F BETHGE
Aachener Nachrichten,
1954

#2

147. A GRIN
2nd Prize, *Shakhmaty
Baku,* 1986

#2

148. G KODER
Ujevi Lap,
1974

#2

149. J SCHEEL
Morgenbladet,
1932

#2

150. I SOLHEIM
Schachvärlden,
1935

#2

151. RAL
Original

#2

152. A PIATESI
L'Italia Scacchistica,
1971

#2

153. RAL
Original

#2

CORNERED

I have always been intrigued by those miniatures where the tetchy brute inhabits a corner. White is constrained to attack from only three directions, yet a myriad of possibilities exist. Long ago, inventive problemists were cramping besieged royalty into reclusive digs. **145** has a protective cocoon of stewards adjoining the sitting duck. Here is an engrossing poser. How can White's queen do battle when forced to keep a bead on 1. ... Ra4? 1. Qe8 (2. Qxb8) is a chipper conclusion. 2. Qxa4 bumps-off 1. ... Ra4+, while the b-rook will be snared wherever he goes. Theodor Herlin pioneered an intricate *modus operandi* with battery formation in 1845. He thusly became one of the earliest innovators to have a "theme" designated in his honor.

146 has opposing officers buffaloed by 1. ... B~ 2. Q(x)b1 and 1. ... S~ 2. S(x)c2. However, 1. ... c3! signals a free ride. White can trip over his own feet 1. Qc2? (2. Qb2, Qc3) because 1. ... Sd1! 1. Qa8! harshly skewers the bishop so that 1. ... c3 admits 2. Sb3. Generally, pinning Black force denotes an offensively strong key. But there should be no reproach for immobilizing an already paralyzed piece.

A phantom 1. ... Ba2+! dares White to play 1. Qa3+? in **147.** This episode has double dares go first. 1. Qc3! summons 1. ... Ba2+ to flick the insect bite 2. b3. Other bishop peregrinations (or 1. ... Ka2) are squashed 2. Qa3.

148 is a thoroughly appetizing teaser. Black's king perches like a bird on a wire and his noble liegeman is held at bay. But nothing can stunt the a7 inchworm from slinking forward. Poetic justice gets served when 1. Sc8 (2. Rxa7) terrorizes that sluggard. The rook is ever grateful to be unpinned but can only flail in vain — 1. ... Rxc8 2. Rxc8 and 1. ... Rb7 2. Sb6.

In **149,** the ebony prince is exiled to a muggy coop escorted by that unbridled palfrey. The knight defends ably against the brusque raid 1. Qf2? (2. Qg2) Sf4! 1. Ra7! weasels three variegated payoffs — 1. ... S~ 2. Qc1, 1. ... Sg3 2. hxg3, and 1. ... Kxh2 2. Rxh5. Each individual unit instigates a personalized model mate.

CROSS PURPOSES

Cross-check has White interfere with an onrushing adversary while simultaneously rendering the kill. **150** shows "direct return captures" which are not dignified as cross-checks. 1. ... Rc7+ 2. Kxc7 changes after 1. Qb1 (2. Qb8) to 2. Sxc7 and 1. ... Rh8 affords 2. Qb7.

A sordid 1. ... Qa8+ mars **151.** 1. Kxg7 (2. Sf6) assuages somewhat through self-pin of bishop. Cross-checks then unlatch for 1. ... Qb2+ 2. Bf6 and 1. ... Qb7+ 2. Be7. The blunt 2. Qxg5 liquidates 1. ... Qxg5+.

A salient bundle of tries populates **152.** The constant intent is an irresistible (2. Sb6). 1. Kb4? a5+! 1. Kc5? Qg5! 1. Kd4? Qd8! 1. Kc3! authorizes 1. ... Qg7+ 2. Sf6 or 1. ... Qg3+ 2. Se3, and 2. ... Bxd5 wolfs down 1. ... Qxd5. Together, those four orthogonal shuffles are styled "king's cross."

DALTON THEME

This baroque complex has White unpin a Black unit, which then skivers the key piece, tit for tat. **153** has phony starts 1. Qe5+? Kh4 2. Qg5, but 1. ... g5! and 1. Qe2+? Kh4 2. Qxh2, but 1. ... Sf3! The correct 1. Qe6! 2. Qh3) is stopped 1. ... g5, but 2. Rh3 takes over. 2. Qg4 beats 1. ... Sf3. It must be noticed that 1. ... g5 refutes without pinning by simple "square vacation." A moot technical point is raised whether this constitutes a certified Dalton.

154. RAL
Original

#2

155. A C WHITE
The White Rooks,
1910

#2

156. RAL
Original

#2

157. RAL
Original

#2

158. RAL
Original

#2

159. M LESCHEMELLE
Europe Echecs,
1996

#2

160. K-P ZUNCKE
Land og Folk,
1979

#2

161. I SHANAHAN
The Problemist Supplement,
1997

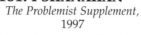

#2

162. R BUKNE
Sjakk-Nytt,
1946

#2

Dead Letters

Line openings and closings are major building blocks in the modern repertoire. They can appear incidentally as subplots or shape a fundamental motif. Russian experimentation began around 1928 and proliferated with further development. There was such a dazzling array of ideas tumbling about, it became uniform to establish alphabet labeling. "Full plate" productions commonly wreak perplexing muddles. Not so in the miniature, but respectable presentations are few and far between. I dredged up five diagrams which exemplify the basic spirit of the highly favored "A" and "B" concepts. Theme A cropped up quite unexpectedly in **154.** The primitive purpose was to have two brawny threat tries shouldered aside by a cool waiter. 1. Qg1? (2. Qg6) is caught flat-footed 1. ... Bg5! 1. Rg8? (2. Bg6) emends 1. ... Bg5 2. Qxg5, but 1. ... Bg7! The insouciant 1. Re6! lounges for 1. ... B~ 2. Bg6. The corrective theme A defense comes with 1. ... Bg5 severing the queen's guard of h6. Then 2. Bg6? would jeopardize rook protection of the same. 2. Qd1 takes advantage of the self-block.

Another theme A defense occurs as if by accident in **155.** 1. Rf4 repositions for 1. ... S~ 2. e4, 1. ... Se4 2. Rf5, 1. ... Sc4 2. Rb5. The latter variation cuts guard of d4 so 2. e4? would disastrously interfere with the other rook guard. Alain White was the foremost proponent of chess problem activity America has ever seen. He carried on a voluminous correspondence with kindred souls the world over. A leading light of the Good Companions epoch, he documented lively, incisive scholia in a torrent of books. *The Christmas Series* are classics of a truly dedicated enthusiast. He amassed a private cache of over two hundred thousand problems. The collection became so unwieldy that it was later subdivided to the charge of several curators.

Levman defense portrays a slightly more sophisticated type of theme A. The threatening unit cloaks a line upon which Black interferes. **156** begins 1. d6 (2. d7). 1. ... Rg3 obstructs so 2. d7? compromises the queen's hold on c7 — it crumples to 2. Qe8. Two other washouts are 1. ... Rd8 2. Qb7 and 1. ... Sb6 2. Qc7.

Theme B is the literal converse when Black opens a line whereby White closes another. **157** has 1. ... S~ allow additional c7 guard so 2. Sb6 can interfere with the bishop. 1. ... Sd6! counter punches with Levman interfering with the rook's line to d8. 1. Rd5 ruins that fantasy by 2. Rc5.

158 bears theme A defense to 1. Re2? (2. Sg3) Sf2! Oddly, Black knight moves revert to theme B after 1. Rh4! S~ 2. Sg3.

Degrees of Separation

The fifteen following problems show various ways whence threats are denied or sundered. **159** starts off 1. Sg2 where 1. ... B~Northwest permits 2. Qe3, 2. Qc2, 2. Re1, or 2. Sf4. 1. ... B~Northeast cancels 2. Qc2 entirely with "partial" separation of the other three. 1. ... Bd2 discards all bringing a newcomer 2. Qc4. 1. ... Kf1 and 1. ... Kd1 are repressed 2. Qe1 and 2. Qd3.

Fleck separation ensures fully unique mating integrity. **160** has 1. Bh6 parade (2. Re1, Rxd3, Rd2, Rc1). They must come singly — 1. ... Sb3 2. Re1; 1. ... Sc2 2. Rxd3, 1. ... d2 2. Rxd2, and 1. ... dxe2 2. Rc1.

1. Sf4 offers two grottoes but energizes that battery to spew (2. Se2, Sf3, Sh3) in **161.** Black's passive bungling credibly deflects any dual choices. 1. ... e2 2. Sxe2, 1. ... Kxc1 2. Sf3, and 1. ... Ke1 2. Sh3.

162 commences 1. Sbd1 posing triplet threats (2. Sf2, Qg4, Sc3). Again, indolent plays force exclusive endings - 1. ... Se2 2. Sf2, 1. ... Sf3 2. Qg4, and 1. ... Sh3 2. Sc3.

163. W HOEK
2nd HM., *Leninska Molodi,*
1967

#2

164. C JONSSON
Smasaker-Hugskott,
1991

#2

165. S KIRILLOV
Problemist Zhoga,
1996

#2

166. O DEHLER
Chemnitzer Tageblatt,
1927

#2

167. RAL
Original

#2

168. S EKSTRÖM
Schachvärlden,
1944

#2

169. G MALEIKA
3rd HM., *Deutsche
Schachzeitung,* 1982

#2

170. I SHANAHAN
The Problemist,
1996

#2

171. M MCDOWELL
The Problemist,
1996

#2

DEGREES OF SEPARATION (CONT'D)

White rallies a mighty host in **163.** Painstaking care banishes repeat mates after 1. Ra4. Five bishop volleys percolate from the battery. They are harmoniously rationed by a Black knight successively smeared under the careening juggernaut 1. ... Sa2 2. Bxa2, 1. ... Sb3 2. Bxb3, 1. ... Sd3 2. Bxd3, and 1. ... Se2 2. Bxe2. A final fillip is 1. ... Kg4 where 2. Bf1 abrogates h3 asylum.

164 trots out an even heftier army. The inhibiting 1. Qc4 is unfortunately necessary. Composers are justifiably rankled when lofty creations must be abased by wretched keys. Four rook fusillades are poised — (2. Rh5, Rhe6, Rae6, Ra5). Again a wandering minstrel delimits projected encroachments by way of 1. ... Sc7 2. Rh5, 1. ... Sd6 2. Rhe6, 1. ... Sf6 2. ae6, and 1. ... Sg7 2. Ra5.

165 thrills with a grandiose outcome. Prepared mates are 1. ... Rxd1 2. Qxd1 and 1. ... R~file 2. B(x)e2. 1. Qh8 confounds totally through priming four downward spouts from a nascent battery — (2. Re4, Re3, Re2, Rxe1). Each soft tread of Black's rook requires singular treatment *à la* Fleck — 1. ... Re4 2. Rxe4, 1. ... Re3 2. Rxe3, 1. ... Re2 2. Rxe2, and 1. ... Rxd1 2. Re1. This portion should be compared with # 413. And there's more with 1. ... Rxe5 2. Qxe5, 1. ... Rf1 2. Rf5, 1. ... Rg1 2. Rg5, and 1. ... Rh1 2. Rh5. Two sets get changed and there are eight distinct post-key mates. To the skillful Ukrainian, Stanislav Kirillov, I say — bravo!

Secondary Fleck dissects supplementary mates stashed in abeyance. **166** has 1. Qh8 skirt the board's outermost rims. White interpolates 2. Qa8 on the heels of 1. ... Sa3, 1. ... Se5, 1. ... Sb2, and 1. ... Ka5. 1. Qa1 zooms in after 1. ... Ka3, 1. ... Sa5, or 1. ... Sb6. Separation is only partial as leftover stragglers 1. ... Sd6, 1. ... Sd2, and 1. ... Se3 extend a choice.

167 has 1. Qh8 differentiate parallel mating apogees *in toto.* 2. Qa8 follows 1. ... Sa5, 1. ... Sb4, 1. ... Sd4, 1. ... Se5, and 1. ... Se7. Then 2. Qa1 mops up 1. ... Sa7, 1. ... Sb8, and 1. ... Sd8.

An opening threat in **168** motivates minatory follow-ups. 1. Qc4 (2. Qxa2) rousts Black's equine squire from his lodging. Were the knight to simply disappear, White's queen could plunk on c2, d3, e4, or f1. But actual arrivals disperse mates precisely — 1. ... Sc1 2. Qc2, 1. ... Sc3 2. Qd3, and 1. ... Sb4 2. Qf1. 2. Qe4? gets completely blackballed from sharing in the mayhem. I would rate Sven Ekström's handiwork as the most splendid secondary Fleck of its kind.

Combinative separation tabulates a docket of mates wholly, singly, or in conjunction. While miniature praxis can only subsume threesomes, larger venues have successfully juggled four direct or secondary threats. **169** shows an omniscient master in this area. A set 1. ... Sf6 2. Qe7 is spiked by 1. Qb5? (2. Qd7) when 1. ... Sf6! secures. A flight-giving 1. Qg4! parlays an overwhelming triad (2. Qc8 **A**, Qd7 **B**, Qxg8 **C**). Black's seven moves assign 1. ... f6 **ABC**, 1. ... Sh6 **AB**, 1. ... Bxb7 **BC**, 1. ... Ke8 **AC**, 1. ... Sf6 **A**, 1. ... Se7 **B**, and 1. ... f5 **C**.

The Australian ace stages a pleasingly original sequence in **170.** 1. Sg5 initiates (2. Se6 **A**, Sxh3 **B**, Qe4 **C**). Meticulous distribution attaches to 1. ... Sa5 **ABC**, 1. ... Sd6 **AB**, 1. ... Sd8 **BC**, 1. ... Bf1 **AC**, 1. ... Bg2 **A**, 1. ... Sc5 **B**, and 1. ... Bg4 **C**.

171 incorporates an "elimination mate." after 1. Ke2. White's jagged trine of (2. Qg4 **A**, Qe3 **B**, Qe5 **C**) is measured out 1. ... g4 **ABC**, 1. ... f6 **AB**, 1. ... f5 **BC**, 1. ... Sf5 **AC**, 1. ... Sf3 **A**, 1. ... Sg6 **B**, and 1. ... Sg2 **C**. 1. ... Kd4 spurns those tendrils to bring a new bogey 2. Qd3.

44

172. R A LINCOLN
The Problemist,
1995

#2

173. I SHANAHAN
Original

#2

174. R A LINCOLN
Smena,
1996

#2

175. K KOMAREVCHEV
Zarya,
1991

#2

176. R A LINCOLN
Magadanskaya pravda,
1997

#2

177. RAL
Original

#2

178. R A LINCOLN
Newark Star-Ledger,
1986

#2

179. R A LINCOLN
Newark Star-Ledger,
1999

#2

180. R A LINCOLN
*Australian Chess Problem
Magazine,* 1996

#2

Degrees of Separation (cont'd)

White material is strictly budgeted in **172.**A bishop duo and rook manage the escapade without blemish. Each Black defender swats prefatory depredations. 1. Ra8? (2. B~) Sf6! 1. Rb4? (2. Rh4) e4! 1. Rb3? (2. Rh3) Kh2! 1. Bf4! synthesizes (2. Rh8 **A**, Rb1 **B**, Be4 **C**) which are apportioned 1. ... e4 **ABC**, 1. ... Sc5 **AB**, 1. ... Sf8 **BC**, 1. ... Sb6 **AC**, 1. ... exf4 **A**, 1. ... Sf6 **B**, and 1. ... Sxb8 **C**. Find this cherished amulet on the cover!

The segment concludes with **173,** a consciously offbeat slant on separation. 1. Sh6? is snubbed because an intrepid 1. ... Bxe6! succors. 1. Se3! complaisantly takes the bishop gremlin in tow through 2. S(x)g2 **A**, 2. Q(x)g4 **B**, or 2. S(x)f5 **C** which all swipe 1. ... Bg2. Sequels then dwindle with 1. ... Bg4 **AB**, 1. ... Bf1 **BC**, 1. ... Bxe6 **A**, and 1. ... Bf5+ **C**. This madcap scattering is yclept "split progressive separation" by Ian Shanahan. 2. Qxf2 exterminates 1. ... Sf2 and 1. ... Sg3 grimly despairs to 2. Qf6. Such an unorthodox scenario definitively breaks the mold and may inspire future cultivation.

Dive-Bombers

Irascible commentators remorselessly lampoon out-of-play key pieces as being extracted from "cold storage." But there can be many hazards infesting illusory tries. Obviously, **174** must drag that slumbering bishop into some usefulness. 1. Bc6? (2. Bg2) is a flash in the pan since 1. ... Rg7! 1. Bd1! (2. Qg4) bodes well with four defenses slumping to 1. ... Se3 2. Qg3, 1. ... Sxh2 2. Qxh2, 1. ... Rg7 2. Qh6, and 1. ... Rh4 2. Qxf1.

An offside bishop is ostensible key candidate for **175.** 1. Ba4? (2. Qc2,Qd1) malfunctions to 1. ... b3! 1. Bd3? (2. Qc2) fares no better against 1. ... b3! 1. Be2! (2. Qd1) hits the mark where defiance is vetoed 1. ... Bc1 2. Qd3 and 1. ... c2 2. Qe1.

176 has a ruefully unemployed queen reclining in an external billet. Three calls to the colors are deflated 1. Qg3? (2. Qa3, Qb3) b4! 1. Qd6? (2. Qa3) Rb4! 1. Qg8? (2. Qb3) Rc4! At last, 1. Qf8! (2. Qa3) puts the kibosh on 1. ... b4 2. Qe8 and 1. ... Rb4 2. Qa8.

A knight has two brave dive-bombing missions crippled in **177.** 1. Sg6? with (2. Qf4, Qe5) doesn't frighten 1. ... Bc7! 1. Se6? (2. Qf4) would foil 1. ... Bc7 2. Sc5, but 1. ... Be3! White keeps his nose to the grindstone by 1. Sd7! (2. Qe5), fulfilling a sleek Barnes theme mosaic. 2. Sc5 is again cocked for 1. ... Bc7 and 1. ... Bd4 sputters to 2. Qf3.

Dream Teams

This discursive treatise touts four White pairings of queen in league with different aides. The pawn gets deputed for three examples. **178** is a sentimental pet, one of my first published miniatures. Black is not bothered by either 1. Qb1? (2. Qxd1) Bb3! or 1. Qd2? (2. Qxd1) Bb3 2. Qd7, but 1. ... Kb3! The blasé 1. Qc4! placidly awaits 1. ... B~ 2. Q(x)c2, 1. ... Bb3 2. Qxa6, 1. ... a2 2. Qxa2, and 1. ... a5 2. b5.

The extraneous a3 pawn of **179** is suggestive. It could only act to curtail a complimenntary aperture contingent upon the hypothetical 1. ... Ka4. Therefore, 1. Qe6 (2. Qb3) obligingly forswears a4 guard for the nonce. Three variations debouch from a slender ensemble — 1. ... a4 2. Qa6, 1. ... c4 2. Qc6, and 1. ... Ka4 2. Qc4.

180 adhibits five facile queen mates in close quarters. 1. f3 (2. Qh7) sows the seeds for 1. ... Bd3 2. Qh3, 1. ... Kh6 2. Qg6, 1. ... Sf8 2. Qxg5, and 1. ... Kh4 2. Qg4. This is yet another of those exasperating straits which problemists despise. The pert mating microcosm gets vitiated by a shoddy key.

181. D G KAISER
Jung-Roland-Rätsel,
1938

#2

182. M VLASOV
1st HM., *Smena,*
1989

#2

183. A RAGANIS
Rigasche Rundschau,
1934

#2

184. R A LINCOLN
Die Schwalbe,
1997

#2

185. V ZAGORUYKO
4th HM., *Molot,*
1971

#2

186. W SPECKMANN
Tidskrift v.d. K.N.S.B.,
1957

#2

187. W SPECKMANN
Deutsche Schachzeitung,
1975

#2

188. S LOYD
New York Evening Telegram,
1890

#2

189. N FADEEV
Insorets,
1982

#2

DREAM TEAMS (CONT'D)

The queen and bishop compartment begins with **181.** Here is a bare bones landscape suffusing a devilishly abstract quandary. How does White make any progress? A daring desertion, 1. Qe7, rebounds with (2. Qa3) wherever the tormented klutz goes to expire.

182 attains considerable mileage from a perfunctory milieu. The slippery 1. Bf3 menaces immediate recouping (2. Qg4) of an interim h3 flight. 1. ... Bh3 blocks to collate the picturesque model, 2. Qd8. Accepting that sullied port by 1. ... Kh3 dispenses 2. Qh7. White's king occupies a fortunate locale by deterring an ever insidious dual 2. Qh8?

My fascination with miniatures did not begin in earnest until purchasing *Miniature Chess Problems*, St. Martin's Press, New York, 1981. This captivating book, by British writer Colin Russ, remains my steadfast reference source. The author's presentation of subject matter is informative, entertaining, mirthful, and never dull. I became permanently hooked on his multitude of little rascals. I don't suppose my mania for miniatures will ever flag. One position from the volume especially piqued my interest. **183** is keyed by a marvelous bishop vault 1. Bc7 (2. Qh2). These debacles are custom tailored — 1. ... Sf3 (or 1. ... Sg2) 2. Q(x)g2, 1. ... Sc2 2. Qb7, and 1. ... Rxc7 (or 1. ... Rh8) 2. Q(x)h8. Each unit is immaculately sited. Knight and pawn hedge against incipient checks. That f7 utensil also cordons Black's second rank in the 1. ... Rxc7 variation.

A quiet nudge, 1. Qf2 (2. Qh4), culls a motley of mates from **184.** Black's d6 loyal associate either unguards 1. ... Be7 2. Qh2, or self-blocks 1. ... Bg3 2. Qxf1. Another block, 1. ... g3, sends a diligent queen 2. Qf5. Finally, 1. ... Bxg2+ 2. Qxg2 plucks the turkey clean.

Limpet mines cling to every Black twitch in **185** — 1. ... Kc4 2. Bf1, 1. ... d4 2. Qb3, and 1. ... c4 (or 1. ... Ke3) 2. Qd2. But any untoward jostle relaxes the grip. 1. Bh1? Kc4! 1. Bf3? Ke3! 1. Kc1? d4! Only the docile 1. Ke1! leaves things unperturbed.

An orderly bishop removal in **186** tweaks opposing knight sentinels. 1. Ba5 (2. Qd8) goads Black into perpetrating empty follies. 1. ... Sf~ 2. Q(x)e6, 1. ... Sd7 2. Qxa6, and 1. ... Sc7+ 2. Qxc7. White had to practice caution as 1. Bb6? would have enabled 1. ... Sd7!

The queen/rook installment kicks off with **187.** 1. Rd1 (2. Qd2) ties a sash on 1. ... Kf2. Aren't solvers being cheated by such puerile fluff? In fact, virtual play inflates this trumpery with emphatic meaning. A rare "White Grimshaw" evolves on d2 after pell-mell checking sprees. 1. Rd2+? Kg1! because 2. Qc1? is blinkered. 1. Qd2+? concedes kiosks on the first rank since 2. Rd1? is closed off. This is unbelievable sorcery using four men.

Sam Loyd, was the beloved "Puzzle King," who took diabolical joy in pulling the solver's leg. He was tricking out positions with counterfeit lures long before the modern vogue of "thematic tries." 1. Ka3? seems so intelligent in **188.** Welcoming gates open wide for 1. ... b6 2. Qh1, 1. ... g7 2. Qh8, but 1. ... c4! 1. Rb3? (2. Kb5) has Black's king fight back by 1. ... Ka2! The rigorous 1. Ka5! (2. Kb6) brooks no pardon.

White's queen takes two bewitching, albeit wrongful jaunts in **189.** 1. Qf1? (2. Qxb5) e5 2. Qf7, but 1. ... Ke5! 1. Qg1? has 1. ... e5 2. Qg8, 1. ... Ke5 2. Qg5, but 1. ... b4! 1. Qa1! hies 2. Qa5 after 1. ... b4, while 1. Qa2 crushes 1. ... e5. The battery fires 2. Rc5 to humiliate 1. ... Ke5.

190. R A LINCOLN
Die Schwalbe,
1996

#2

191. W SPECKMANN
3rd HM., *British Chess
Magazine,* 1973

#2

192. R ASPLUND
Tidskrift för Schack,
1957

#2

193. R A LINCOLN
Prize e. a., GAMA Ty,
1995

#2 (b) Sc4>a8
     (c)Sc4>g4

194. J GASPAROVIC
British Chess Magazine,
1988

#2

195. C SENECA
La Stratégie,
1933

#2

196. R A LINCOLN
*Australian Chess Problem
Magazine,* 1997

#2

197. W E F FILLERY
Canandian Chess Chat,
1982

#2

198. R A LINCOLN
diagrammes,
1998

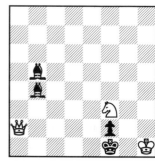

#2

DREAM TEAMS (CONT'D)

White has three deviant trails to storm Black's cozy manor in **190**. 1. Qg2? toils for 1. ... f6 2. Qg6 and 1. ... Kf6 2. Qg5, but 1. ... S~! sniggers at the lame sortie. The knight also nips 1. Qf3? (2. Qxf4) Se6! 1. Re7! befuddles the arrogant dragoon where 2. Rxf7 is loaded to shoot upon his exodus. Other reprisals go 1. ... f6 2. Qh5, 1. ... f3 2. Qxf3, and 1. ... Kf6 2. Qe5.

191 has a charming vicissitude with try and key piece touring the same spot. 1. Rg6? has a flush forecast for 1. ... B~ (or 1. ... Rg1) 2. Qe2, and 1. ... Kg1 2. Qe1. Alas, Black ekes out 1. ... Be5! The unerring 1. Qg6! imposes 1. ... B~ 2. Qg2, 1. ... Rg1 2. Qd3, and 1. ... Kg1 2. Re1. This time around, the hopeful savior 1. ... Be5 bombs to 2. Qd1.

Solvers may be reluctant to part with the crisply embossed set replies of **192**. 1. ... Ba7 2. Rxc7 and 1. ... c6 2. Rxc6 seem like sure things, but Black's light-square bishop luxuriates in smug equanimity. 1. Rd8 burdens that piece to the liability of averting 1. ... Bc~Northeast 2. Qb5 and 1. ... Bc~Northwest 2. Qd5. Set mates are discreetly altered by 1. ... Ba7 2. Qxc7 and 1. ... c6 2. Qd4.

193 shoehorns three banal ploys into one concordant blend. The first portion confirms 1. Kc7 (2. Re7) with a goodly total of defenses 1. ... Se5 2. Rd6, 1. ... f6 2. Qd5, and 1. ... f5 2. Qe7. White takes a new tack in part (b) where 1. Qf4 (2. Rd6) coerces another pawn "one-two" couplet 1. ... f6 2. Qe4 and 1. ... f5 2. Qd6. The final phase milks yet two more propositions through 1. Rd5 (2. Qf5) — 1. ... f6 2. Qg8 and 1. ... S~ 2. Q(x)e5. Each Black knight rotation accommodates solution from a different key piece. Nine distinct mates get tallied altogether. This providential aggregate is the consequence of judicious twinning.

White queen and knight flexing in tandem are often an exceedingly fruitful partnership. Sixteen spry configurations span nefarious doings of this dynamic union. Queen and knight teamed to nag the hermit king of #136. **194** spreads three mates by simply inducting a Black pawn. There is an ironclad imperative to guard b5. So the give-and-take 1. Sd5 doles out 1. ... b5 2. Qa2, 1. ... Ka4 2. Qb4, and 1. ... Ka6 2. Qxb6.

The French composer Camil Seneca investigated numerous ways to employ two Black pawns. **195** sports one brittle set mate 1. ... e4 2. Qd6. This must assent to 1. Kd3 with a "spoof" threat (2. Qd6) negated 1. ... e4+ 2. Qxe4. It is confusing to classify this peculiar *objet d'art* as mutate or block-threat.

Three Black foot soldiers are strewn in **196**. 1. ... c3 is fraught with 2. Qc5 but other pawn moves are harmless. 1. Sc7 (2. Sb5) causes a twinkling realignment for 1. ... c3 2. Qd5. 2. Qd2 hustles to collar 1. ... Kc3 and 2. Qxe3 belts 1. ... e3.

197 links a horizontal chain of pawns. 1. Qh4 ferries the secluded queen to espy (2. Qd4). The threat is never realized as 1. ... c5 2. Qe4, 1. ... Kc5 2. Qg5, and 1. ... e5 (or 1. ... Kc5) 2. Qc4. 2. Qd4 could be actualized by excluding White's knight and planting a Black pawn at b6. Most presumably, the author wished to have 1. ... Kc5 2. Qa5 under control.

In **198,** White contends with a bishop pair. No tries are afoot, but the sober 1. Qe6 (2. Sh2) spools off three diverse defensive gaffes. 1. ... Bd6 is direct guard rapidly penalized by 2. Sd2. 1. ... Bc6 pins the knight redounding to 2. Qc4. The last variation has a cunning 1. ... Be2 cut the queen's sight of e1. The resultant self-block propels 2. Qh3.

199. V POPONIN
Comm., Bron MT,
1993

#2 (Version by RAL)

200. R A LINCOLN
Newark Star-Ledger,
1998

#2

201. B ELMGREN
2nd HM., *Springaren,*
1953

#2

202. R A LINCOLN
StrateGems,
1998

#2

203. R A LINCOLN
StrateGems,
1998

#2

204. R A LINCOLN
StrateGems,
1999

#2

205. J FULPIUS
Journal de Genéve,
1951

#2

206. RAL
Original

#2

207. A OLENIK
Leninski plemya,
1989

#2

DREAM TEAMS (CONT'D)

199 again has White vying against two bishops. Paradoxically, it is Black's pawn who obviates a sturdy try 1. Sh6? (2. Sf7, Sg4) with 1. ... f3! The only way to dispute that flight-opening prospect is 1. Sh4! where the threat (2. Sg6) smothers f4. Opposition consists of one humdrum unguard, 1. ... Be8 2. Sf3, plus self-blocks 1. ... Be4 and 1. ... Bd4. These are hassled respectively by 2. Qd6 and 2. Qf5.

I managed to chisel three defensive travails from Black rooks in **200**. 1. Se6 (2. Qd8) prods those lumbering louts into treacherous deadfalls. 1. ... Rd5 lets the knight cavort merrily on with 2. Sxc7 as does 1. ... Rc8 2. Sxg7. To finish up, there's a perennially reliable self-block through 1. ... Rd7 2. Qf8.

Two rugged Black knights picket the perimeter of **201**. 1. Sd5? (2. Qb4) is felled 1. ... Sc6! 1. Sc2? (2. Qb4) bounces innocuously against 1. ... c5! A pitiless 1. Sc4! lays the matter to rest with an incongruous waiter. The death rattles are 1. ... Sa~ 2. Q(x)b5, 1. ... Sb~ 2. Q(x)a3, and 1. ... c5 2. Sb6.

StrataGems is America's premiere chess problem periodical. The driving catalyst behind this quarterly magazine is chief editor Mike Prcic. He has enlisted an excellent staff to handle a cornucopia of originals in every category. He also provides many pages of special features from a host of able contributors. I composed **202** for an article showing the White queen/knight clique facing a Black party of rook, bishop, and pawn. Hence, each type of unit is represented. The direct 1. Qf2? (2. Qh2) gets sternly repulsed 1. ... g3! 1. Sg6? (2. Qxh4,Sf4) is similarly decked, 1. ... g3! It takes the nondescript

1. Qe4! to shatter all four comers — 1. ... g3 2. Qh1, 1. ... B~ 2. Q(x)g2, 1. ... R~ 2. Qxg4, and 1. ... Kg3 2. Qe3.

Another gratifying flight-giving key adorns **203**. 1. Sf4 (2. Qe2) galvanizes a convivial compound of desolate bungles. 1. ... Rh2 forsakes the first rank for 2. Qf1. 1. ... Re1 is that ever hardy self-block giving 2. Qxa4. At length, 1. ... Bb5 opens a portal with 2. Qa1 on tap.

My article alluded to the fact that this material ordains practical limits. Four discrete finales is usually the maximal output. I would later feel contented after inadvertently hitting upon an apt proposal. **204** hatches a whimsical Rube Goldberg contraption into grinding out a coveted fifth mate. The demoralizing, but necessary 1. Se4, resuscitates the knight from deep freeze. Black's plenary corps is trussed up 1. ... R~ 2. Q(x)h7, 1. ... Rh6 2. Qg4, 1. ... f5 2. Qg5, 1. ... B~Northwest 2. Sxf6, and 1. ... B~Southwest 2. Sg3.

205 can only justify White's knight with an inflexible g6 landing. 1. Qh5? furthers this aim when 1. ... S~ grants the desired 2. Sg6. But Black stays alive by 1. ... g5! An opportune 1. Qh1! veils the h-file ordering, but 2. Sg6 still wins over enemy knight moves. 2. Qa1 caroms to snuff 1. ... g5 with a kitty-corner mate.

That unprovided cavity, 1. ... Ka3, of **206** is an irritating blot. However, 1. Sc6 (2. Qb4) atones somewhat by tendering a flight offer on b5. 1. ... Ka3 stumbles into 2. Qa1 and 1. ... Kb5 is pummeled 2. Qc4. Bishop aid is ineffectual since 1. ... Bc5 2. Qa5.

A disciplined bump by White's king dooms Black's fiesty flock in **207**.

208. R A LINCOLN
Magadanskaya pravda, 1998

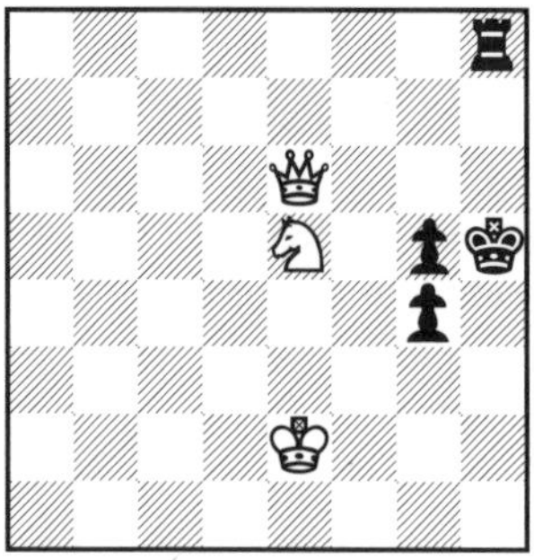

#2

209. RAL
Original

#2

210. RAL
Original

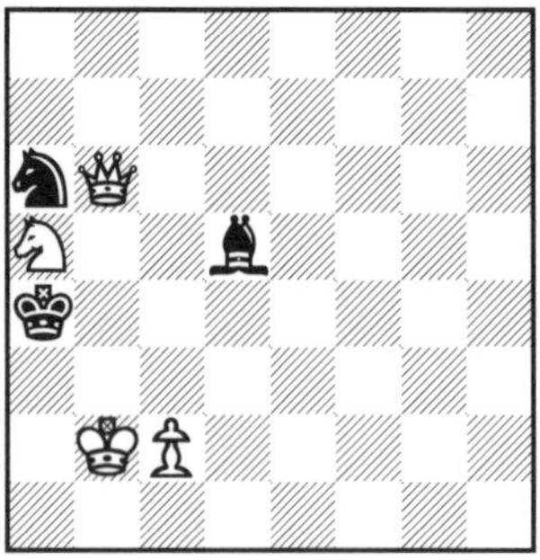

#2

211. R A LINCOLN
3rd Comm., *Smena,* 1995

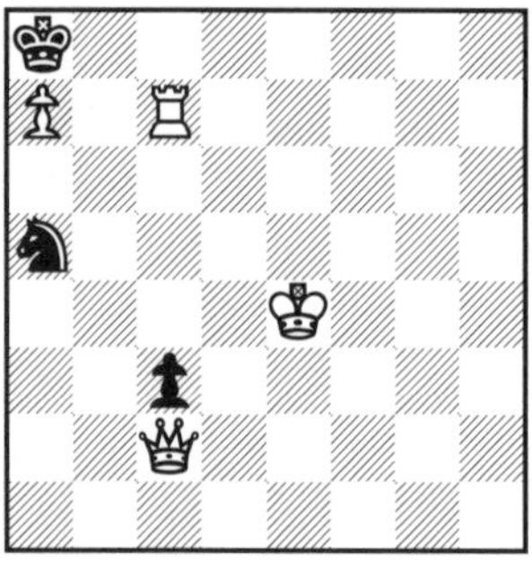

#2

212. R A LINCOLN
The Problemist Supplement, 1999

#2

213. M LIPTON
The Problemist, 1992

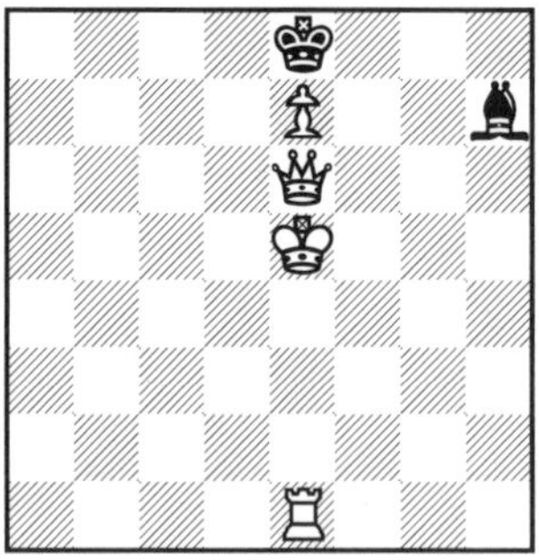

#2

214. N ZINOVYEV
3rd HM., *Lisove gospodarsto,* 1994

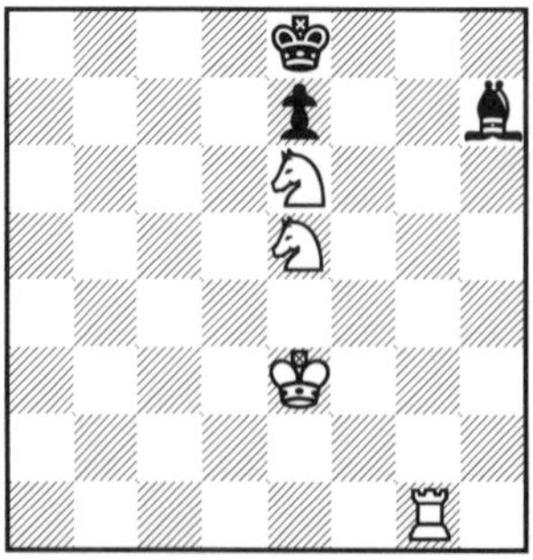

#2

215. L GROLMAN
Probleemblad, 1998

#2 (b) Bb2=P

216. R A LINCOLN
Magadanskaya pravda, 1997

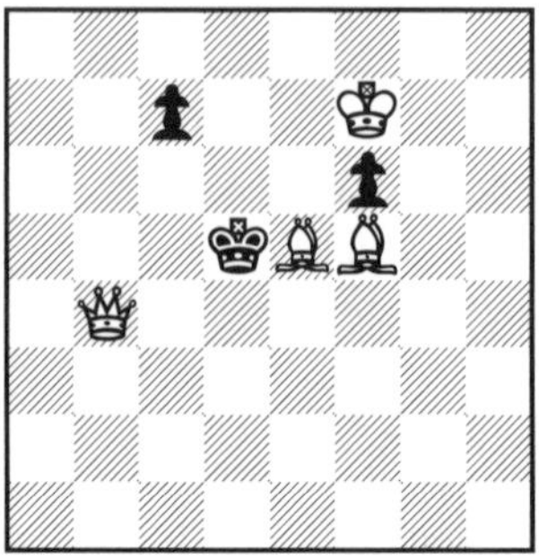

#2

DREAM TEAMS (CONT'D)

Most of Black's fluttering choices are already under a cloud in **208.** 1. ... g3 2. Qh3 and 1. ... Rh6 (or 1. ... Kh4) 2. Qxg4 omit one desperado, 1. ... R~! 1. Qf5 saps that last ditch acquittal by 2. Q(x)h7. The newly opened claim to 1. ... Kh6 is befouled 2. Qg6.

It appears very unlikely that White's knight of **209** will checkmate. But a wholesale readjustment matures rapidly. 1. Qb8 exposes the teensy chink to focus on (2. Qb4). Now, 1. ... a5 is knocked for a loop with 2. Sc5. Two supplementary bailouts are subverted 1. ... Sd5 2. Qb5 and 1. ... Ka5 2. Qxa7.

DUELING BANJOS

"Thematic" tries are the sum and substance of modern two-movers. If White essays the same piece throughout, a nice graphic unity is curried. It becomes more pointed when Black's refutations involve but one defender. A panorama of single combat burgeons with each side consistently dueling to outstrip his opposite number. **210** is a rustic case where knight and bishop square off. (2. Qa5) is the constant threat when White's cavalier goes trucking about. His hopscotch gets brazenly bashed without mercy — 1. Sb7? Bxb7! 1. Sc6? Bxc6! 1. Sc4? Bxc4! 1. Sb3! is quite a different story because 2. cxb3 retards 1. ... Bxb3.

White's queen unfurls four refulgent ventures in **211.** A chancellor adeptly wards off 1. Qb1? (2. Qb8) Sc6 2. Qb7, but 1. ... Sb3! 1. Qxc3? (2. Qh8) Sb7! 1. Qf2? (2. Qf8) Sc6! The jaunty colt cannot withstand 1. Qa4! (2. Qe8) Sc6 2. Qxc6 and 1. ... Sb7 2. Rc8.

White's "common aim" is (2. Qxb7) during a fourfold fracas in **212.** The intractable rook antagonizes an invading queen. 1. Qe7? Rg7! evinces the need to attack c8 as well. 1. Qc7? encumbers a site the knight craves after 1. ... Rb8! 1.

Qxc6? keeps secondary options available, but 1. ... Rg6! savagely pins. 1. Qd7! infallibly chastises 1. ... Rg7 2. Qc8 and 1. ... Rb8 2. Sc7. One more crumb, 1. ... S~ 2. Qa7, makes the whole loaf.

213 is the most expansive duel one could ever imagine. Seven rook tries are stultified by the bishop matching his movements indomitably. 1. Rh1? B~ 2. Rh8, but 1. ... Bg8! 1. Rg1? B~ 2. R(x)g8, but 1. ... Bg6! 1. Rf1? (2. Rf8) Bf5! 1. Rd1? (2. Rd8) Bd3! 1. Rc1? (2. Rc8) Bc2! 1. Rb1? (2. Rb8) Bxb1! 1. Ra1? (2. Ra8) Be4! All shadowboxing is for naught as 1. Kd6! solves. 1. ... B~ meets a jejune demise, 2. Q(x)g8. Only the grumpy purist would deride such a skylarking carnival of camouflage.

Superficially, **214** looks as though rook and bishop will mount the same hobbyhorse. Indeed, a slugfest follows the general pattern shown previously —1. Rh1? Bg8! etc. This time 1. Rg7! puts the damper on 1. ... B~ 2. R(x)g8.

DUPLICATION

Uncompromising dilettantes take extreme umbrage at dual mates. But there are situations where the defects of repeat blows can be transformed into a virtue. The amenable **215** leverages a battery into place by 1. Rb1. Flights and blocks complement each other with symmetrical chic — 1. ... a5 (or 1. ... Kc5) 2. Ba3 and 1. ... c5 (or 1. ... Kc5) 2. Bc3. Downgrading bishop to pawn in part (b) gives 1. b3 with similar pairings 1. ... a5 (or 1. ... Kc5) 2. Qc4 and 1. ... c5 (or 1. ... Ka5) 2. Qa4. The outlying rook still has a role by guarding d6 in the 1. ... Kc5 line.

Self-blocks occur on diagonal and orthogonal niches in **216** 1. Ke7 waits out 1. ... c5 (or 1. ... Kxe5) 2. Qe4 and 1. ... fxe5 (or 1. ... Kc6) 2. Be4. One added block, 1. ... c6, skids to 2. Qd4.

217. T SWEENEY
L'Italia Scacchistica,
1970

#2

218. RAL
Original

#2

219. R STEINMAN
Blumenthal
Schachminiaturen, 1902

#2

220. R ALIOVSDZADE
& M VAGIDOV
Mat, 1980

#2

221. A DIKUSAROV
StrateGems,
1998

#2

222. RAL
Original

#2

223. F C BETTS
Good Companions,
1916

#2

224. N SIOTIS
Canandian Chess Chat,
1982

#2

225. R A LINCOLN
3rd Prize, *Australian Chess*
Problem Magazine, 1996

#2 (b) Sc6>b1

DUPLICATION (CONT'D)

Several ways are suggestive whereby White can torpedo Black's leaky vessel in **217**. 1. Qe7? negotiates 1. ... c6 2. Qa7, but 1. ... Ka5! 1. Qa2? (2. Qa7) Kc5! 1. Qe5? (2. Qb5) effaces those hegiras, but either 1. ... c6! or 1. ... c5! are adequate. A caustic 1. Sa6! brokers two alternate chalets in return for pilfering of those troublesome a5/c5 squares. Black's pawn "one-two" dovetails with king flits — 1. ... c6 (or 1. ... Kxa6) 2. c5 and 1. ... c5 (or 1. ... Kc6) 2. Qe6.

So far, examples have bracketed the flights with pawn hedges. **218** attains a more checkered miscellany of *leitmotivs*. 1. Qe5 (2. Qxe7) persuades both 1. ... Bd8 (self-block) or 1. ... e6 (line-opening) to engender 2. Qh5. 1. ... Bb4 (line-unguard) or 1. ... Kd8 (self-interference) license 2. Qb8. The *en prise* queen is a niggling handicap in an otherwise cheerful position.

EVER ONWARD

Here are a few problems all utilizing pawn keys. There are really no grounds for disparaging less difficult prologues. **219** starts off with a lackadaisical 1. g3. One finds nary a hint of timorous try. This quirky foible would be arbitrarily dismissed by choosy editors today. But in 1902, the norm seldom smacked of sophistication. A routine tabulation is easily assimilated — 1. ... d3 (or 1. ... Ke5) 2. Qf4, 1. ... Kd3 2. Qf3, and 1. ... f5 2. Qe2.

220 has a cogent jab 1. Sc6? (2. Qd4) Sf3! That knight is a hapless onlooker after 1. f4! (2. Qc4) Ke4 2. Qd3. This soupçon of cotton candy is hardly symbolic of the collaborating authors. These gentlemen, along with I. Likumovic and J. Vladimirov, conceived a colossal prototype for the "Vladimirov theme" (1977). # 413 is a shorthand exemplar appearing within this volume.

Things become a tad more interesting with **221** although 1. g4 sticks out like a sore thumb. When the unpinned ranger advances 1. ... f4, bells ring for 2. g5 to steam ahead. Extirpating that pest 1. ... fxg4, translates to self immolation 2. Bxg4. Finally, White's g-pawn repays in spades after 1. ... g5 2. gxf5. This waggish *tête-à-tête* between two plebian sprites is highly entertaining.

1. h4? (2. Qg5) chases a mirage in **222**. 1. ... Sg4 looks encouraging since 2. Qd3, but 1. ... Sf7! defuses any damage. 1. h3! is a shorter prop which shanghais the knight to expiry through 2. Q(x)g4. That dolorous g-pawn uncorks further carnage by 1. ... g6 2. Qf4 and 1. ... g5 2. Qd3. The latter variation recasts a zestful mate transference.

Calculating mentalities can nourish the en passant rule into ripe florescence. **223** reaches an acme of perfection. 1. b4 spins three pleasurable mates — 1. ... a3 2. Qc2, 1. ... axb3 *e.p.* 2. Qa1, and 1. ... Ka3 2. Qxa4. The Good Companion Chess Problem Club was founded by James Magee Jr. of Philadelphia. The society prospered from 1913 until 1922. At its peak, this global organization boasted over six hundred members.

224 is really just an *en passant* joke. Nonetheless, this may very well be the only way to exploit double captures from White. 1. f5 snips 1. ... e5 2. fxe5 *e.p.* or 1. ... g5 2. fxg5 *e.p.*

A White pawn "one-two" can be magnified when try and key swap after twinning. **225** goes 1. c4? (2. Qa3) Sb4! 1. c3! cuddles gladly to thwack 1. ... S~ 2. Q(x)b4 and 1. ... a5 2. Qxc6. Part (b) causes a methodical about face — 1. c3? (2. Qb4) Sxc3! 1. c4! waits with confident hauteur for 1. ... S~ 2. Q(x)a3 and 1. ... a5 2. Qb5.

226. J SZOGHY
Die Schwalbe,
1979

#2 (b) after key of (a)
  (c) after key of (b)

227. E SZENTGYÖRGI
Funkschach,
1926

#2

228. T R DAWSON
Chess Amateur,
1920

#2

229. J KAPROS
1st Comm., GAMA Ty,
1995

#2

230. A AZHUSIN
*4th HM., Radyansko
Slovo,* 1973

#2 (b) Sg7>e7 (c) Sg7>h3
  (d) Sg7>e5

231. L KARLSSON
Folket,
1947

#2

232. R A LINCOLN
diagrammes,
1997

#2

233. T SCHÖNBERGER
Magyar Sakkvilág,
1933

#2

234. R ASPLUND
2nd Prize, *Norsk Vanfore,*
1954

#2

EVER ONWARD (CONT'D)

White's d-pawn does not start his perambulation until the twinned portions of **226.** First, there's is a give-and-take 1. Qd3 which eggs the prey to a cul-de-sac, 1. ... Kf4 2. Qf5. This rather amorphous jape is barely enough to carry its weight. Events perk up in part (b) which has no appropriate "waiter. " 1. d6 derisively shunts the victim to 1. ... Ke6 with 2. Qf5 again called into service. Then (c) is yet another riddle which dares not disturb the balance. So it's ever onward, 1. d7, whence a changed 2. Qd6 abducts 1. ... Ke6.

EVER UPWARD

And now, four breezy models of pawns hankering for coronation. **227** has Black's knight mired under promotional sludge — 1. ... S~ 2. c8+Q and 1. ... Sc8 2. b8=S. One can readily guess there's bound to be moderate renovation. 1. b8=Q prefigures an unconditionally puissant, but startling ricochet, 1. ... Sc8 2. Qb5.

2. b8=Q will be the quietus after 1. ... Kxe8 in **228.** But White's garrison is fixed in frozen postures. Only a lowered investiture, 1. b8=S, breaks the deadlock. Then 1. ... Kxe8 glumly droops to 2. Qg8. Thomas Rayner Dawson had a meteoric career as chess problem popularizer. His editorial posts were associated with *The Chess Amateur*, *The Problemist*, and *British Chess Magazine*. Founder and guiding spirit of *Fairy Chess Review*, he single-handedly made esoteric forms intelligible and enjoyable for thousands of devotees.

Minor promotions grace **229.** 1. d8=B untethers the woebegone knight for 1. ... Se7 2. Bxe7, else (2. Bf6). Part (b) sees a bishop overawed by 1. d8=S (2. Sf7). These humorous highjinks emit a bouyant stamp of originality.

The German term *"Allumwandlung"* describes successive pawn conversions to every possibility. **230** needs three rearrangements with one unit happily oscillated about. (a) goes 1. f8=Q Kh6 2. Rh5. (b) has 1. f8=B Kh8 2. Rh5. (c) solves by 1. f8=R Kh6 2. Rh8. Finally, (d) proceeds 1. f8+S+ with 2. Sf7 arriving for 1. ... Kh8 or 1. ... Kh6. Strategic acuity may be missing, but the twinning device is an imaginative triumph.

FAVORITE GROUP

The White queen, accompanied by both bishops, combine effectively versus two Black pawns. This doughty strike force finds usage in what seems infinite settings. **231** has a commonplace flight-giver, 1. Qf6, appended with a threat (2. Qxd4). Furious scrambles are dashed 1. ... e5 2. Qc6, 1. ... Ke4 2. Qf3, and 1. ... Kd6 2. Qd8.

232 can afford to be more chivalrous via a dillydally waiting move. 1. Qf6 wheedles the lummox into false security as hospitable coves are contaminated — 1. ... Kd5 2. Qxe6 and 1. ... Ke3 (or 1. ... Kd3) 2. Qxd4. Pawn pushes are harried 1. ... e5 2. Qf3 and 1. ... d3 2. Bf3. The latter sprig glistens with sneaky line-opening plus self-block.

The drab detainee is firmly manacled in **233.** That h6 "plug" suggests an abeyant mutate, but 1. Bg3 implicates (2. Qd3). This menace also wrestles 1. ... Ke3 and 1. ... Kf3 to the mat. 1. ... Kd4 is walloped 2. Qe5.

Concluding farragoes have various contortions of Black pawn "one-two." **234** restricts all options by 1. ... f6 2. Bh6, 1. ... f5 2. Be7, and 1. ... Kf6 2. Qf5. The e4 stopple fundamentally counsels mutate solution. A scintillating 1. Bd6 changes 1. ... f6 to 2. Bf4. 1. ... Kf6 is now soured by 2. Qh6.

235. b ellinghoven
Deutsche Schachzeitung,
1971

#2

236. W SPECKMANN
Die Schwalbe,
1995

#2

237. V PILCHENKO
1st HM., *Smena,*
1997

#2

238. A PETRUSENKO
3rd Prize, Lokker MT,
1975

#2

239. R A LINCOLN
Newarl Star-Ledger,
1998

#2

240. Z ZILAHI
Magyar Sakkvilág,
1927

#2

241. RAL
Original

#2

242. RAL
Original

#2

243. N P BUDKOV
Due Alfieri,
1984

#2

FAVORITE GROUP (CONT'D)

A number of gritty tries vivify **235.**
The queen seeks a commanding sphere
through 1. Qd4? (2. Qxg7), but 1. ... Kg6!
squirts away. 1. Qg3?, again scouting g7,
has 1. ... g6 2. Qc7, but 1. ... g5! fortifies.
A waiter, 1. Qf3?, larrups 1. ... g6 2. Qf7,
but 1. ... Kh8! abides. 1. Qh3! cuts the
Gordian knot with a further answer to 1. ...
g6 2. Qd7. Three other mates are deco-
rously indexed — 1. ... h5 2. Qxh5, 1. ...
g5 (or 1. ... Kg6) 2. Qf5, and
1. ... Kh8 2. Qxh6.

236 has a pair of sham starts. 1. Qf5?
would continue 1. ... b5 2. Bc5 and 1. ... e5
2. Qd7, but 1. ... e6! rescues. A two-step 1.
... e5! blights a 1. Be1? (2. Bb4) try. The
punctual 1. Bh4! (2. Bxe7) collects 1. ... e6
2. Qd4 and 1. ... e5 2. Qc6.

An identical consummation occurs in
237 after 1. Bd8 (2. Bxe7). There is a triv-
ial difference where 1. ... e5! jams the
screeching brakes on 1. Ba5? (2. Bb4) or
1. Bf7? (2. Qe6).

In this section, the best was saved for
last. The notion of three phase (or more)
mate changes against two (or more) Black
moves has been examined by composers
unremittingly. Changes may happen in set
play and a try, or in tries exclusively.
Called "Zagoruyko," the program generally requires a big palette. Small renditions
belong within a class of *rara avis* destined
to live on as imperishable lodestones.
Such is my reaction to **238.** 1. Qf5? rec-
onnoiters for 1. ... e3 2. Bc3 and 1. ... Ke3
2. Qf2, but 1. ... c5! 1. Bg2? has altered
replies for 1. ... e3 2. Qc3 and 1. ... Ke3 2.
Qd2, but again 1. ... c5! stands fast. It takes
1. Bg3! to lance 1. ... c5 by 2. Qd2. Then
1. ... e3 and 1. ... Ke3 capitulate to 2. Qe5
and 2. Qc3. Repetition of that 2. Qc3
through mate transference makes the
process subtitled "reduced Zagoruyko."

FIGHTING PIECE

Wilhelm Steinitz once referred to the
king as a "fighting piece." Four items
show White's king initiating action. It is
usually *de rigueur* to infringe on the counterpart's field as **239** does. 1. Kc3 (2.
Qd4) is simply too strong. But there is a
euphoric trio of self-block defenses — 1.
... Be4 2. Qd6, 1. ... e5 (or 1. ... Kc5) 2.
Qc4, and 1. ... c5 2. Se7.

240 is much more pleasing as the king
"fights" by taking leave of the area.
Black's knights are under house arrest —
1. ... Sh~ 2. Q(x)g8 and 1. ... Sc~ 2.
Q(x)e7. Only 1. Kb6 keeps tabs on those
results. An extra souvenir is 1. ... Kd8 2.
Qf8.

King keys are never objectionable if
part and parcel of a try continuum. **241**
has 1. Kf4? approach with dual mischief,
(2. Bg5, Rh2), which Black sunnily taunts
1. ... e5! 1. Kf5? threatens just (2. Bg5),
but 1. ... e6+! discombobulates. 1. Kf3!
tamps down (2. Rh2) which cannot be
denied. The purposeful point is "Barnes
theme" concatenated with pawn one-two
refutations.

In **242,** Black's royal presence wears a
mantle of pawns. Each White king ascent
bolsters (2. Qe3). 1. Kf2? is wanting
because of 1. ... Kd4? or 1. ... f4! 1. Ke2?
improves by watching d3, but 1. ... Kf4!
hearkens to the siren song of g4 haven.
Final rectification is 1. Kd2! The laundry
list includes 1. ... f4 2. Qd3, 1. ... d4 2.
Qf3, and 1. ... Kd4 2. Qb4.

FLIGHTS OF FANCY

I gathered these twenty-nine positions
where escape routes form the major thematic content. **243** has diagonal exits
molested without a participating White
queen. 1. Rc6 ratchets the springe for 1. ...
Kd5 2. Bf3, 1. ... Kf5 2. Bc2, and 1. ... Kd3
2. Sf2.

244. A FINK
Chess Life,
1980

#2

245. E ERNST
Badische Neuste
Nachrichten, 1993

#2

246. RAL
Original

#2

247. N GIORDANO
Chess Life,
1957

#2

248. K KOMAREVCHEV
Rassvet Severa,
1997

#2

249. M VLASOV
Smena,
1994

#2

250. M REITMAN
Troll,
1993

#2

251. F LAZARD
Bulletin Federation
Francaise d'Echecs, 1926

#2

252. V KOSEK
Narodny Listy,
1900

#2

FLIGHTS OF FANCY (CONT'D)

Black's majesty in **244** is bereft of kith and kin. The dark square outlets at c5 or e5 whet inquiry as to would-be bishop arrivals on b6 or f6. But White's queen hurries apace for those locations instead. 1. Qh6 shepherds a submissive gudgeon to 1. ... Kc5 2. Qb6 and 1. ... Ke5 2. Qf6. The short-lived legacy on third rank is cleaved by 1. . . Kxc3 (or 1. . . Kd3) 2. Qd2. Experienced solvers will root out the undemanding plot with no difficulty. Still, such an innocuous nicety amuses a general audience.

A few measly pawn tokens can make a dramatic difference. **245** starts another waiter with the predictable give-and-take 1. Qg4. A gloomy, derelict king is thrice violated by his own acolytes — 1. ... f6 2. Qe6, 1. ... f5 (or 1. ... Kd5) 2. Qd4, and 1. ... d5 2. Qf4. A last crowning indignity goes 1. ... Kf6 2. Qg5.

Quite often problems are struck off following much uncertain trial and error. But others have their genesis with concrete aforethought. **246** is one of these. I dreamt up ways in which Black pawns would self-block while unguarding to allow knight mates. A half-baked grope, 1. Re4? (2. Rxf4) Kf3 2. Qxf4, but 1. ... Kf5! is a meaningless distraction. The insouciant 1. Re2! holds Black in thrall. Either 1. ... Kf3 or 1. ... Kf5 founder to 2. Qh5. The pre-conceived variants click perfectly — 1. ... f5 2. Se5 and 1. ... f3 2. Se3. An offside knight intruder seems a cheap price to pay.

Black hugs four guilt-free resorts in **247**. After 1. Qa1, a bruising queen rides roughshod over the gimpy harlequin. 1. ... Kf4 2. Qe5, 1. ... Kf2 2. Qg1, and 1. ... Kd2 (or 1. ... Kd3) 2. Qc3.

White's d-knight of **248** is a tasty *bonne-bouche*. It's in for a dime or in for a dollar with 1. Sd3. Both snacks are verboten 1. ... Kxd5 2. Qd7 and 1. ... Kxd3 2. Qc3. The brief session is adjourned with 1. ... b4 2. Qc4.

I became intensely enchanted when first encountering **249**. An unpretentious scenario yields a stupefying key, 1. Qd4. Despite the sudden munificence of two flights and a spare trinket to play with, Black is dumbfounded. The pawn toady self-destructs 1. ... c6 2. Qb6 and 1. ... c5 2. Qa4. If the dreary king scampers, he is run to ground by 1. ... Kc6 2. Qd5 and 1. ... Kxa5 2. Qc5. There's no dual 2. Qa4? attending that last twig since the guard on b6 went poof.

White would be content to pass in **250**. A steely grip worsts 1. ... Ke3 2. Qe5 and 1. ... Kd4 2. Qf4. But 1. ... c2! putters harmlessly. 1. Sc2 may seem a clumsy means to balk that clodhopper. Further, the "set" vestibule is confiscated. What the enemy receives in return are alternate dead ends 1. ... Kd5 2. Sxc3 and 1. ... Kd3 2. Bf5. This unconventional opus artistically inserts minor proxies in lieu of queen mates.

251 has a freakish styling which evinces a notable happenstance. 1. Qh7 entreats the cursed king to fly 1. ... Kd7, 1. ... Kxe8, 1. ... Kxe6, and 1. ... Kf7. All nestling places are annihilated 2. g8=Q. This montage of four orthogonal "plus-flights," is seldom attained in miniature. The lavishly generous first move marks a bravura spectacle.

Many composers get caught up with the so-called "Y-flight." This trendy grid has Black's king welcome to an orthogonal window and two diagonal ones in the opposite direction. **252** is a flashy demonstration from days of yore. 1. Ke7 waddles into the fray to fate 1. ... Kd5 2. Qf3, 1. ... Kf5 2. Bd3, 1. ... Ke3 2. Qe2, and 1. ... d3 2. Qxd3.

253. S ZIMMERMAN
Sport a Hry,
1908

#2

254. J MAYHEW
*The Problemist
Supplement,* 1992

#2

255. R NOTARO
The Problemist,
1980

#2

256. I MURARASU
The Problemist,
1991

#2

257. L TRYSSESOONE
The Problemist,
1984

#2

258. H DES MARANDS & P MONREAL
1st Prize, *La Marsillaise,* 1945

#2

259. RAL
Original

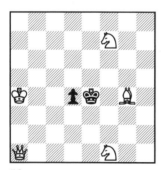

#2

260. C W M FEIST
Hampshire Magazine,
1884

#2

261. E GOLDSCHMIEDT
Pesti Naplô,
1927

#2

FLIGHTS OF FANCY (CONT'D)

The antique **253** has been emulated repeatedly. Zimmerman's rendition is the earliest I could find of this particular y-flight jewel. All exits are untended at the outset and there is not a scintilla of a try. Yet, it contains an indelible charm ranking among classics. 1. Qd7 queues on 1. ... Kxd3 2. Se3. That exterior knight is outfitted to clock 1. ... Kc5 2. Se6 and 1. ... Ke5 2. Sf3.

The Problemist Supplement is an excellent medium where fledgling composers can disseminate their wares. Editor Brian Stephenson has been the vibrant force behind this publication since 1992. His announced aim is to encourage newcomers to the art. There is nothing complex about **254.** Veteran solvers will doubtlessly plank down 1. Rh5 in a jiffy. Nevertheless, such a guileless bauble soothes savage breasts with winsome flow — 1. ... Ke3 2. Rh3, 1. ... Kg4 2. Qd1, and 1. ... Kg2 2. Qa8.

The next three positions appeared in *The Problemist*. This prestige magazine is official organ of the British Chess Problem Society. Policy has always favored a sizeable forum to showcase quality miniatures. **255** is one of few y-flight specimens taking the bull by the horns with an actual threat. 1. Qe3 must continue (2. Sd2) against 1. ... Kc4. The gadabout bronco also romps for 1. ... Kc6 2. Sc5 and 1. ... Ke5 2. Sg3.

The h6 bishop of **256** should kindle abundant curiosity. Its sole vocation must be to mind g7 and g5 lest Black gains f6 access. 1. Qb4 grants leeway whereupon 2. Qxd6 snipes at 1. ... Kf6. The rest of the dominoes fall 1. ... Kd7 2. Qg4, 1. ... Kd5 2. Bf7, and 1. ... d5 2. Qe7.

Readers may tire of watching that sleepwalking jerk funneled into dismal execution chambers. However, the artistic well never dries up. **257** utilizes a rook/bishop combo to laudable effect. 1. ... Kf4 2. Re4 is safely in the bank. 1. Bc8 conquers the oblique squares through 1. ... Kh3 2. Re2 (direct battery) and 1. ... Kxh5 2. Rh6 (indirect battery). Lamentably, this was one of the last problems by the Belgian virtuoso, Louis Tryssesoone.

A capital y-flight mechanism gets an honored trophy in **258.** 1. Sh4 (2. Qf3) uses the threat to mangle 1. ... Ke3, and 2. Qxg1 dispenses with 1. ... Kg3. Most intriguing is 1. ... Kf1, self-pinning that lickspittle bishop. Then 2. Qf3? would unpin permitting 2. ... Bf2! Hence, 2. Rf4 whisks over to profit from the pin. See numbers # 349-351 for other examples of this defense, Nietvelt theme. A final sweet-meat is 1. ... Bh2 2. Qe1.

A nearly symmetrical **259** grooms swift appointments for 1. ... Kf4 2. Qxd4 and 1. ... d3 2. Qe5. White's king is needed to track lagging cloisters. 1. Kb4 jerry-builds a short queen tilt 2. Qb1 at 1. ... Kd3 and a "long-shot" 2. Qa8 for 1. ... Kd5.

Four free diagonal offerings encompass "star-flight." Herewith are eleven layouts of varying texture showing this historically influential protocol. An old memento is **260,** a six-man aristocrat. Typical of this genre, 1. Sd5 takes one flight while giving two back. 1. ... Kf5 (or 1. ... Kd3) 2. Qg6, 1. ... Kxd5 2. Qd4, and 1. ... Kxf3 2. Qg2.

261 surpasses by releasing three of the sockets while obtaining none for recompense. White prizes open unique mates for all spokes of the quadrant — a *sine qua non* of respectable star-flights. In fairness, 1. Qe8 is stark necessity, so to crimp 1. ... Kf4 2. Qe3. "Gift" squares are infected with 1. ... Kf6 2. Qe7, 1. ... Kh6 2. Qg6, and 1. ... Kh4 2. Qh5.

262. V ANTIPOV
Serp i molot,
1987

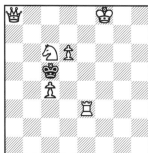

#2

263. A R POIRE
Chess Life,
1983

#2

264. G BAKCSI
Marcius Tizenfodike,
1948

#2

265. V CHAIKO
Shakhmaty v SSSR,
1987

#2

266. B LORINC
Nepszava,
1942

#2

267. M KLASINC
1st Prize, *Delo,*
1970

#2

268. F HOFFMANN
Revista de Sah,
1967

#2

269. M MCDOWELL
British Chess Magazine,
1995

#2

270. L ISKRA
64,
1970

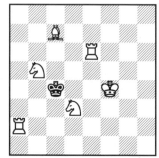

#2 (b) Kf4>c1

FLIGHTS OF FANCY (CONT'D)

271 has an allied crux with a baleful rook coming in from the sticks taking potshots. This time White's queen is responsible for all but one of the mates. Part (a) goes 1. Ra5+ Ke6 2. Re5, 1. ... Kg6 2. Qxg7, 1. ... Ke4 2. Qf4, and 1. ... Kg4 2. Qg3. The clone has Black's sovereign residing in refurbished quarters. Then the attack swivels underneath 1. Rg1+ with 1. ... Kf5 2. Qe5, 1. ... Kxh5 2. Qh2, 1. ... Kf3 2. Qf4, and 1. ... Kh3 2. Qg3.

FOUR OF A KIND

Several items are grouped together featuring four units of the same or different color. **272** has horses evenly cribbed into their pens. Black is about to be stampeded by 1. ... Se~ 2. S(x)g6 and 1. ... Sg~ 2. S(x)e6. White's king isn't used for patrol duty, so 1. Kg5 tiptoes sedately away to maintain stasis.

A little more excitement is generated by **273**. White has padlocks for both clefts — 1. ... Kd7 2. Qc8 and 1. ... Kf6 2. Qh6. There's a dire prerequisite to rope in Black's gypsy steeds. 1. Qf4? veers close by commandeering the d6 and f5 squares. But 1. ... Kd7! treks off unimpeded. 1. Qc5! scores by keeping glimpse of c8 to corral 1. ... Sb~ 2. Q(x)d6 and 1. ... Sd~ 2. Q(x)f5. The prearranged hit for 1. ... Kf6 delightfully changes to 2. Qe5.

A fifth knight is necessary for conquest in **274**. 1. d8=S plants another exigent guard on b7 so that 1. ... S8~ 2. S(x)c6 and 1. ... S6~ 2. S(x)c8 understandably follow. This particular setting has a perspicuous resemblance to # 272.

The witty gambol of **275** doesn't get the fourth knight until White's coup. 1. f8=S+ sends the crestfallen emperor into the clutches of 1. ... Kd6 2. c8=S. Less melodramatic is 1. ... Kc8 2. Se7.

My researches for examples of rook, bishop, or pawn troupes were fruitless. So I was obliged to draft these quixotic aberrations. Composing "on demand" sometimes leads to unforeseen vagaries. **276** has 1. Kf3 trundle forward to shore up (2. Qe4). 1. ... Ke5 uncovers protection from the h7 cleric. But interference with the c7 colleague can then be spooked 2. Qf4. More illustrative open-and-shut cases are to be found in the segment on valves.

Another king irruption motivates **277**. 1. Kd6 rips terribly bellicose double threats (2. Rxa8, Rxg8). The demure point is no duals occur. Testing any of Black's nine plays verifies that singularity of mate is assured.

Four pawns barely cooperate in a serviceable problem. **278** contains the unadorned essentials with makeshift bric-a-brac. 1. Qg5 is adequate to unceremoniously dump 1. ... Kd4 2. Qf4, 1. ... d4 2. d3, and 1. ... e5 2. Qg4.

FULL PRESS

Situations are frequently alluded to throughout this volume as ideal mates. This means every speck in the diagram is "working. " The Black king field can be guarded or blocked only once. An elite magazine, *Ideal-Mate Review*, specializes in these impeccable outcomes. The brainchild of Eugene Albert, issues come every three months and carry approximately two hundred originals. Albert nurtures sources from around the globe. There's a decided leaning to heterodox positions. But orthodox direct mate two-movers make an occasional appearance. **279** goes 1. g5 offering binary flights at f5 and h5 while robbing those at f6 and h6. A pathetic passenger must take that dizzying toboggan slide to 1. ... Kf5 2. Sh4 or 1. ... Kh5 2. Bh7.

280. R A LINCOLN
Ideal-Mate Review,
1998

#2

281. R A LINCOLN
Magadanskaya zavtra,
1999

#2 (b) Bh6>e1

282. N ZINOVYEV
Ideal-Mate Review,
1997

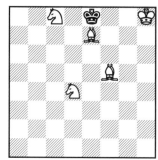

#2 Four solutions

283. L JACOMETTI
L'Italia Scacchistica,
1915

#2

284. R A LINCOLN
Kudesnik,
1999

#2

285. G GUIDELLI
L'Alfiere di Re,
1924

#2

286. F GOROG
Chess Life,
1968

#2 (b) Qf7>g6

287. S SYCHEV
The Problemist,
1991

#2 (b) Bc5>a3

288. L GROLMAN
Problemist pribuzha,
1992

#2 (b) Pd3>b5

FULL PRESS (CONT'D)

It has become increasingly onerous to ferret out intrinsically virgin nuggets in two-mover format. Ideal constraints are severe, and composers have mined the ore for a long time. I chanced upon a possibly original construct in **280.** There's no valid reason for shying away from "obtrusive" bishops if it gets the job done. 1. Bge3 navigates 1. ... Kd5 2. Sc3 and 1. ... Kf5 2. Sd6.

281 is a misbegotten attempt at ideal mirror mate. Mirror refers to a Black king situated where nothing abuts the circumjacent eight squares. In other words, he sees his "reflection" wherever he might turn. Of course, conditions of ideal still apply. 1. Rg6 makes hay bringing 1. ... Ke5 2. Rc5. Regrettably, the second half has a snake in the grass. My intention was 1. Ra6 Kc5 2. Re5 with a pretty "echo" effect. I didn't realize that dual, 2. Ra5, until the position was mailed to Russia — oh well.

Pairs of both knights and bishops are a dainty dish to place before Black's king in **282.** He must perforce slither to 1. ... Kf7 continuously throughout four dapper climaxes. First, there is 1. Kh7 followed by 2. Bg6. Then, 1. Bg4 inserts 2. Bh5. Third, 1. Sdc6 reguards e7 so 2. Sd6 ensues. Lastly comes 1. Sb5 with a bind on 2. Sbd6.

GAMAGE THEME

This theme owes its name to the American problemist Frederick Gamage. He was architect of a convoluted throng with the embryonic idea in 1911. Black interferes with one of his men allowing White to unpin in mating. **283** is an early miniature success. 1. Bh4 zippers up e1 menacing (2. Qxc2). Black's line-pinned queen tries to shield by 1. ... Qd2, whereupon 2. Qf3 surges. King schleps to d2 or e2 are massacred 2. Qxd3.

My **284** maneuvers in similar vein with some faint divergences. Here, the fateful check, 1. Qg6+?, is playable at once. 1. ... Kf8 is haunted by 2. Se6, but the rook has been unchained for 1. ... Rf7! Ergo, 1. Bh6! (2. Qxd7) invites 1. ... Be7 for 2. Qg6, while 2. Qe6 tackles 1. ... Ke7 or 1. ... Kf7.

The esteemed Italian composer Giorgio Guidelli made few miniatures in his tragically short career. Nonetheless, posterity is grateful for **285,** a real humdinger. 1. Kg3 sets the stage for two Gamage interference/unpins 1. ... Sc2 2. Qa8 and 1. ... f5 2. Qh8. Other moves of that knight incur 2. Qxb1.

GEMINI COMPLEX

Twinning, where the same position appears in altered guise, serves two very important purposes. Composers can feel relieved that their gamble may have a credible bid for originality. And solvers, tangling with the shuffled paraphernalia again, get more bang for the buck. **286** begins 1. Be3, where the sorry minstrel is netted by 1. ... Ke4 2. Qe6 or 1. ... Kd6 2. Bf4. Less accordant after the queen switch is a crass flight-taker, 1. e3. Now, 1. ... Kd5 is swamped 2. Qf5.

Black's bishop of **287** is harried to death. 1. Rf4 (2. Qf1) seduces 1. ... Bf2 2. Rxf2 or 1. ... Bg1 2. Qa8. That latter zoom returns in part (b) via mate transference. 1. Re1 ogles (2. Rg1) when 1. ... Bc1 (or 1. ... Bc5) lets 2. Qa8 roll.

288 parlays pawn-one-two madness aplenty. 1. d4? (2. d5, Qe5) gets derailed 1. ... f5! 1. Qf4! gruffly paws 1. ... Kd6 (or 1. ... f5) 2. Qd6 and 1. ... f6 2. Qe4. With c6 covered, White can give d6 away by the cheeky 1. Sb6. Then, 1. ... Kd6 (or 1. ... f5) and 1. ... f6 are capsized by 2. Qe7 and 2. Qd5 respectively.

289. A TAUBER
Chess Review,
1940

#2   (b) Pc3>d3

290. M MCDOWELL
The Problemist,
1984

#2   (b) Sd1>a2

291. M MCDOWELL
The Problemist Supplement,
1996

#2   (b) Bd3>f4

292. J KUBECKA
Ideal-Mate Review,
1991

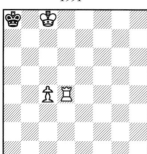

#2   (b)Pc4=B

293. A CASA
3rd Comm., *diagrammes,*
1995

#2 (b)Bc2>b1 (c)Bc2>f1

294. RAL
Original

#2 (b)Pc7>b7 (c)Pc7>b2

295. A DZECKER
Prapor peremogi,
1970

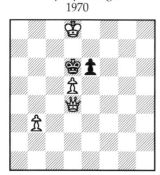

#2 (b)Pb3>e3 (c) Pb3>f3

296. E BOGDANOV
3rd Prize, *Prapor peremogi,*
1972

#2 (b) Kd2>c3 (c) Kd2>d4
(d) Kd2>e3

297. D BANNY
Comm., Krumm MT,
1998

#2 (b) Be4>b5 (c) Rc6>f1
(d) Sh3>h6

Gemini Complex (cont'd)

Readers must know that miniatures only occasionally achieve blockbuster status. More than likely, straitlaced staples such as **289** are par for the course. This austere packet lifts off 1. Qa8 compelling 1. ... Kxc1 for switchback 2. Qh1. The next go around has 1. Qh8 with a threat (2. Qb2) appended to the h1 glissade. Persistent errands to three corners tell the whole story.

290 is a thematic feast in modern style. 1. Sc7 (2. Qd5) lambastes the surly potentate by 1. ... Kc5 2. Qc3 and 1. ... Ke5 2. Qe3. After one knight settles in a new abode, 1. Sf6 (2. Qc3) buttons up 1. ... Kc5 with 2. Qd5. Pattern specialists thrill to such le Grand reversal of threat and follow-through against 1. ... Kc5. Also noteworthy is the upside down "Y" shape of the mating sites.

Michael McDowell has enjoyed good fortune in his rejuvenating of familiar regions. To get anything original from five men with Black pawn promotion is fabulous. **291** has the queen trespass 1. Qe3 for 1. ... e1=Q 2. Bc2, 1. ... e1=S 2. Be2, and 1. ... Ke1 2. Qxe2. The matinee pours on the pressure with 1. Qh2 causing 1. ... e1=Q 2. Qc2, 1. ... e1=S 2. Qe2, and 1. ... Ke1 2. Qg1. Six mates in all — wonderful!

Naturally, White's rook will park on the a-file in **292.** 1. c5 unbars the preemptory stroke, (2. Ra4). The bishop replacement stays put in part (b) when 1. Rd6 goes to slay with (2. Ra6). These shenanigans are cheerless in themselves, yet the twinning idea glitters.

The last half-dozen items have supplementary adjuncts when three or more problems are drawn from the palimpsest. **293** begins cleanly enough, 1. Kg2, with 1. ... Kc4 or 1. ... Ke4 socked by 2. Qc5 and 2. Qe5. The secondary phase has 1. Sc3 make a potlatch of two flights. Then,

1. ... Kc4 (or 1. ... Kxc3) are demolished 2. Qb4, while 1. ... Ke4 (or 1. ... Ke3) gravitate to 2. Qf4. The third retouch is a vapid nonentity as 1. Se3 merely reprises the bookings of part (b).

Lettering may help explain the doings of **294.** White has three promising ways to activate his knight: 1. Sc4 (2. Ra5) **A**, 1. Sd3 (2. Sb4) **B**, and 1. Sc6 (2. Sb4) **C**. Black can euchre any faulty missteps throughout. The initial proviso has **A/B**? wash-out to 1. ... Bb6! and 1. ... c5! **C**! wins over 1. ... Bc5 2. Sb8. The next juncture sees **A/C**? botched by 1. ... b6! and 1. ... bxc6! **B**! is positioned to glom 1. ... Bc5 2. Sxc5. Finally, **B/C**? both fail since 1. ... b1=Q! So **A**! injects 2. Rxb6 against 1. ... Bb6.

295 slots White's backward pixie into amended springboards. First, there is 1. b4 e5 2. Qc5 and 1. ... exd5 2. Qf6. Then comes 1. e4 e5 2. Qb6 and 1. ... exd5 2. Qxd5. The last jump-off has 1. f4 e5 2. fxe5 and 1. ... exd5 2. Qb6.

Black king meandering in **296** paints a handsome cyclic portrait. Four mates are labeled 2. Bg5 **A**, 2. Ba5 **B**, 2. Bf6 **C**, and 2. Bb6 **D**. To start, there is 1.Rd5 with 1. ... Ke3 **A** and 1. ... Kc3 **B**. Secondly, 1. ... Kd4 **C**. Thirdly, 1.Rf2 has 1. ... Kc3 **C** and 1. ... Ke3 **D**. The king's rhomboid shaped internary concludes with 1.Kb2 enclosing 1. ... Kd4 **D** and 1. ... Kd2 **A**.

The fluid matrix of **297** relocates three members of White's delegation. Part (a) goes 1. Rg6 g4 2. Sf4 and 1. ... Kg4 2. Rxg5. Following is 1. Rf6 g4 2. Be8 and 1. ... Kg4 2. Be2. The penultimate round has 1. Rf7 g4 (or 1. ... Kh6) 2. Rh7 and 1. ... Kg4 2. Bf3. Finally, 1. Sg8 devastates 1. ... g4 2. Rh6 and 1. ... Kg4 2. Sf6. Eight separate mates without a queen is pure wizardry.

298. C-E SPARE
The Problemist, 1990

#2 (b) Be1> al (c) Further
Kb1>a2 (d) Further Ba1>a5

299. I GODAL
Magasinet for Alle, 1945

#2

300. F EIDEM
Dagbladet, 1958

#2

301. F H SINGER
The Problemist, 1986

#2

302. T STEUDEL
Schach-Echo, 1965

#2 (b) Pf7>g7
Two solutions each part

303. J KNÖPPEL
Fairy Chess Review, 1947

#2

304. RAL
Original

#2

305. J VALUŠKA
4th HM., Segers 80 Ty, 1995

#2 (b) Sd7>g1
(c) Sd7>d4 and Qb8>h2

306. V LISKOVETS
(v) *64*, 1981

#2

GEMINI COMPLEX (CONT'D)

The process known as "continued" twinning arises in **298**. White's threat stays staunchly riveted on (2. Qb2). 1. Kb3 shows 1. . . Kc1 2. Qa1. (b) affects 1. Kd3 with 1. . . Kc1 2. Qh1. Then (c) has 1. Kc4 assist in 1. . . Ka3 2. Qxa8. Lastly, 1. Kc2 fine-tunes 1. . . Ka3 2. Qa1. Keys form a "king's cross" and swashbuckling queen bounds gladden the heart.

GIMMICKS

Here is a hodgepodge with no unifying bond. They are oddball creations featuring daffy, but humorous flukes. Under promotion by White is a hoary standby as in **299**. 1. d8=Q? would mortify through arrant stalemate. So 1. d8=B! lets the king gallivant into tarnished lairs — 1. ... Kd2 2. Bg5 and 1. ... Kd4 2. Bb6. Mates are "ideal" in both cases.

Not to be outdone, **300** dubs two knights with an ideal state. 1. d8=S gains purchase on f7 for Black's sheepish somnambulism into 1. ... Kg6 2. f8=S.

301 fairly oozes with a mutate flair. 1. ... Kd8 2. Qd7 is irrefrangible, so White must sit on the fence. However, 1. Ke6? is bunged up 1. ... d5! and 1. a8=S+? sees 1. ... Kb8! go unpunished. 1. Sa8+? would trip 1. ... Kc8 2. Qe8, but 1. ... Kd8! This petty sifting identifies the only tenable key as 1. Qa4!, with a lovely postscript, 1. ... Kxb6 2. a8=S.

Oftentimes, that telltale name above the diagram declares what will transpire. When Theodor Steudel spots a seventh rank White pawn, one can predict some wacky promotional gig. **302** rouses a split Allumwandlung. The first pairing has 1. f8=B (2. Rc6) and 1. f8=R Kd6 2. Rf6. The other partition rams home 1. g8=S Kd6 2. Rc6, and 1. g8=Q+ with 1. ... Kd6 2. Qd5 or 1. ... Kf6 2. Qf7.

The vivid totem pole of **303** has a benefit. It can easily be recalled from memory. There's not much to the play. After 1. Qg5, the sullen king withers under 1. ... Kf3 2. Qe3 and 1. ... Kh3 2. Qh4. The gist of this pygmy charade is to demonstrate a symmetrical position with asymmetrical mates.

The dotty **304** engages a tortuous agendum. White self-pins giving a flight square. When Black takes that flight, he unpins for mate. There is but one line, 1. Kb7 Kd7 2. c8=Q. I have never seen this particular strategy before. There seems to be legitimate dimension for expanded query. It might very well find productive scope in a larger undertaking.

305 utilizes an outlandish apparatus. Rampaging keys embroider a crazy quilt fabric which makes sense in the end. Mates are defined thusly — 2. Qg3 **A**. 2. Qf4 **B**, and 2. Sf3 **C**. 1. Sf6+ jumps on the Black king who flutters like a caged canary by 1. ... Kh4 **A** and 1. ... Kg5 **B**. The next phase starts fiercely by 1. Sg3+ mapping 1. ... Kh4 **B** and 1. ... Kg5 **C**. Two relocations are usually frowned upon in twinning. One can readily condone this negligible misdemeanor after 1. Sf4+ returning 1. ... Kh4 **C** and 1. ... Kg5 **A**. The upshot is "cyclic Zagoruyko." Perhaps radical surgery is the only way to achieve this complicated schema in miniature.

HAPPY WANDERER

I have always been mesmerized by the White queen finding all four corners during her travels. Five examples are selected to show these jolly, devil-may-care tours. **306** has a tomfoolery prelude 1. Qd5? (2. Qb3) Ba4! Therefore, 1. Qh8! (2. Qa1) which can zing right past 1. ... Bf7 2. Qa8.

307. F LINDGREN & W KRAMER
Chemnitzer Tageblatt, 1927

#2

308. V KALANDADZE
Problemist pribuzha, 1990

#2

309. A N KIEV
Probleemblad, 1981

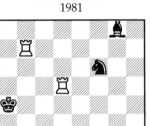

#2

310. RAL
Original

#2 (b) Remove Pg7

311. RAL
Original

#2 (b) Rh1>h8

312. RAL
Original

#2 (b) Bh1>a8

313. R NOTARO
The Problemist, 1978

#2

314. RAL
Original

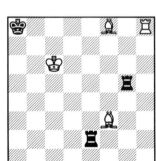

#2

315. K BRAITHWAITE
US Problem Bulletin, 1981

#2 Two solutions

HAPPY WANDERER (CONT'D)

2. Qa8 is already geared for 1. ... Ke4 in **307**. White needs to afflict those other cusps of Black's "star-flight. " 1. Qa1 is the meal ticket for 1. ... Kxg2 2. Qh1 and 1. ... Ke2 (or 1. ... Kg4) 2. Qd1. That a8 shot remains undisturbed.

308 has the ridge-runner hasten over to 1. Qh8. This covert flight-giver shags 1. ... Kxg2 2. Qh3. The other balls drop into the corner pouches on schedule after 1. ... Rxg2 2. Qa1 and 1. ... Rh1 2. Qxh1.

1. Qh8 foments irrevocable calamity for the defenders of **309**. Black's king removes upon a grisly 1. ... Ka3 2. Ra5. His glowering lieutenants must permit 1. ... S~ 2. Qa1 and 1. ... B~ 2. Qa8.

Finally, **310** is a problem where Madame does not sprout from one of the remote nooks. There are visitations to all outermost reaches in try and key twice. The first setting teases solvers with 1. Qf2? (2. Qf7) Bf4! 1. Qh4? (2. Qd8,Qe7) g5! 1. Qa1? (2. Qa8) Bg5! At last, 1. Qh1! (2. Qa8) is the tonic which meanly quenches 1. ... Bg5 2. Qh8. Deducting that g7 ruffian has 1. ... Kf8! go on the lam after 1. Qh1? So it's back to 1. Qa1! (2. Qa8) where 1. ... Bg5 (or 1. ... Kf8) bring 2. Qh8. Tries and threats skate the edges *en rapport*, orchestrating a "pseudo le Grand. "

KINGSTON

The British Chess Problem Society held their annual weekend meeting at Kingston-upon-Thames for consecutive years 1997-1999. These are gloriously festive affairs. The jovial folk come not only from Britain, but many other countries to partake in the camaraderie. Old friendships are rekindled and new ones are formed. Herculean volunteer efforts behind the scenes make everything go smoothly. The 1998 event had a "quick" composing contest as usual. David Shire proposed a two-mover concept which twins by transporting rook or bishop to the opposite side of the board. No one could fathom a miniature on such short notice. Later, allowing some sufficient time for cogitation, I cobbled together the following. **311** has 1. Kh2 slacken the straitjacket to force 1. ... Kh5 2. Kg3. With h1 rook overhead, 1. Bh7 again consigns a robot-like 1. ... Kh5 (or 1. ... Kh3) whereupon 2. Bf5 finishes.

Obtrusive bishops were the expense to be borne in **312**. 1. Rg2 unglues Black's sticky impasse with 2. Rg4 trailing 1. ... Ke4. After the h-bishop's elevation, 1. Rb7 entails a threat (2. Rg4) which archly chops 1. ... Ke4.

MACKENZIE THEME

The "Mansfield couplet" has two Black units controlling a battery. Each in turn self-pins, allowing the compatriot to be shut off. The Mackenzie theme clarifies these ingredients in merger with a checking key. **313** unleashes 1. Kb3+ for 1. ... Ba7 2. Sg3 and 1. ... Ra7 2. Se3. The leftover 1. ... Kb1 necessitates double check by 1. Sd2.

Another royal battery detonates **314**. 1. Kb6+ meshes associated correspondents 1. ... Rd5 2. Be7 and 1. ... Re4 2. Bg7. 2. Bd6 slam dunks 1. ... Kb8.

MANIFOLD DESTINIES

After a hurried squint, one may judge **315** a flat out mutate. 2. Se8 is set for 1. ... Kc7, and 1. e7 enrolls an understudy 2. e8=S. But wait a minute, there is an *embarras de richesse*. 1. Kf8 also solves by keeping the set while prompting 1. ... Kxe6 2. Se7.

316. S RADCHENKO
Idea-Mate Review,
1993

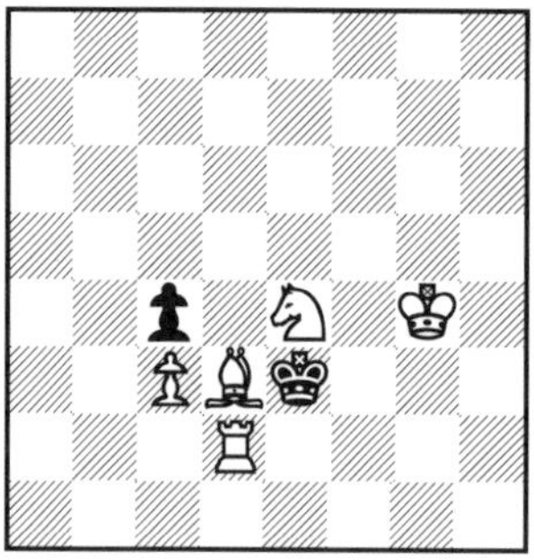

#2 Two solutions

317. M MCDOWELL
2nd HM., *Il Duale,*
1978

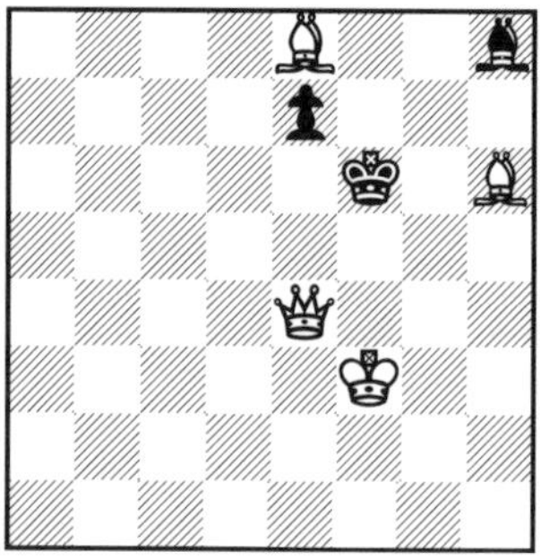

#2 Two solutions

318. M MCDOWELL
Problem Observer,
1989

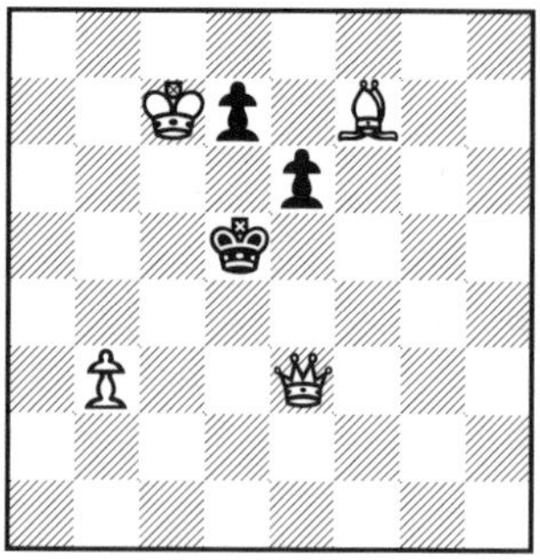

#2 Four solutions

319. C-E SPARE
The Problemist Supplement,
1995

#2 Zero position (a)d4>e3 (b)Pe2>f2 (c)Bf3>f1

320. A SELIVANOV
Problemist pribuzha,
1990

#2

321. RAL
Original

#2 Three solutions

322. R A LINCOLN
The Problemist,
1995

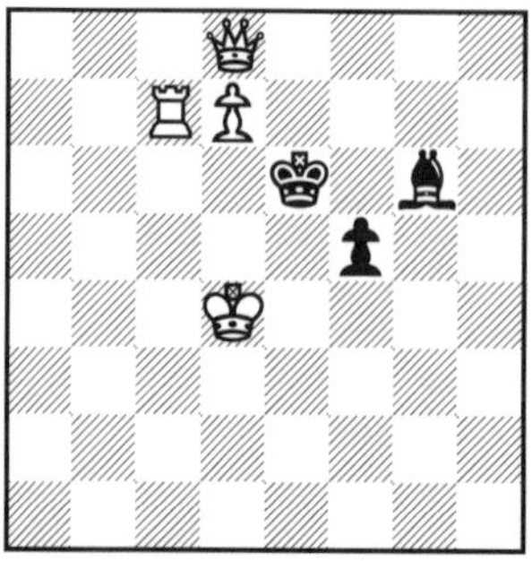

#2

323. R A LINCOLN
Smena,
1995

#2

324. R A LINCOLN
Newark Star-Ledger,
1999

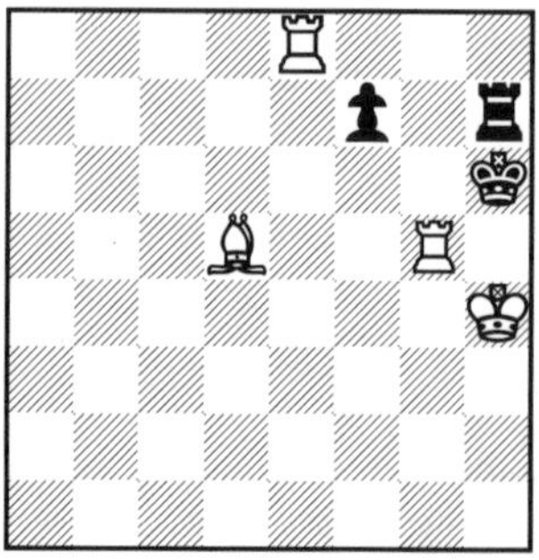

#2

MANIFOLD DESTINIES(CONT'D)

The insolence of two or more keys flies in the face of venerable tradition. But modern connoisseurs take perverse relish in flouting inherited wisdom. If one must shirk conventional tenets, it should be done artistically. Matched byways of **316** fit like a glove. 1. Rd1 prepares for the inevitable 1. ... cxd3 with 2. Re1. Lightning strikes twice on the e-file when the sedulous rook gets 2. Re2 after 1. Bxc4 Kxe4.

To attain full change against three Black self-blocks is nothing short of miraculous. **317** has a lyric sweetness which should guarantee problemistic immortality. 1. Qd5 readies the sinister sequence 1. ... e6 2. Qg5, 1. ... e5 2. Qf7, and 1. ... Bg7 2. Bg5. The alternate 1. Bf8 is better with disguised generosity. Now Black's piddling choices are slated for 1. ... e6 (or 1. ... Kg5) 2. Qf4, 1. ... e5 2. Qg6, and 1. ... Bg7 2. Bxe7. In a related sidebar, Fedor Davidenko got 5th HM for a nearly identical one solution position.

The audacious **318** contrasts four problem types within one capsule. 1. Bg8 ingenuously sits on 1. ... d6 2. Bxe6. 1. Be8 accordingly alters 1. ... d6 to 2. Bc6 while tacking on 1. ... e5 2. Bf7. Next, 1. Kb6 retains the prearranged mate, and infuses 2. Qc5 for 1. ... Kd6. Finally, 1. Bh5 spurts venom (2. Bf3). The complete roll call of categories is waiter, mutate, added mate, and block threat.

"Zero position" twins by changing the stated diagram as well as successors. Double threats have a bad reputation, especially when there isn't any defense whatsoever. Nonetheless, **319** may give food for thought. (a) begins 1. Sg4 and (2. Rg3, Sf2) are invincible. (b) has 1. Se2 wield the overpowering (2. Rf2,Sg3). (c) goes 1. Sf3 whence (2. Rh2, Rg1) rule. This delicious puff pastry amalgamates three knight openings and six different threats.

MAXIMUMS

Eleven positions are included under this rubric. Each stretches to the limit some peculiar aspect. Four mates from a White pawn is nicknamed "albino." This enduring instrument amplifies praiseworthy and recurring commerce in heavyweights. Miniatures always require awkward keys. **320** starts with an unkind 1. Ka4, but the culmination has a silver lining. The pawn struts his stuff by 1. ... Kb2 2. d3, 1. ... B-Northeast 2. d4, 1. ... Bc3 2. dxc3, and 1. ... Be3 2. dxe3. Two more twinkles stud a nonpareil bijou, 1. ... Bb2 2. Sb4 and 1. ... Ba1 2. Qb3.

My **321** is a poorer cousin — three solutions from solitary puppet. 2. Bf4 scorches 1. ... d4 throughout. 1. c3 Ke4 2. Qe6 is stained by a dual 2. Qe8. 1. cxd3 gives 1. ... Kd4 2. Qc3. Best of the bunch is 1. c4 with 1. ... dxc4 2. Bc3 and 1. ... Kd4 (or 1. ... Ke4) 2. Qxd5.

322 shows four promotions by White pawn spread across three phases. Set play deposes 1. ... Bf7 2. Rc6 and 1. ... Be8 2. dxe8=Q. 1. Qf8? (2. d8=S) comes to grief because 1. ... Bf7! is now viable, *i.e.* 2. Rc6? Kxd7! A neat 1. Qc8! (2. d8=Q) jousts for the other knight fling, 1. ... Be8 2. dxe8=S.

A fourfold mating calculus from two rooks is the linchpin of **323.** 1. Rd6? (2. Rd8) accentuates the core obligation to dissuade 1. ... Rb1! Therefore, 1. Rb6! (2. Rb8) whitewashes 1. ... Rb1 by 2. Re8. Black's a-pawn factors in 1. ... a6 2. Rxa6, and 1. ... axb6 2. Ra4.

The natty **324** has three eventual rook scratches surface as try threats. 1. Reg8? (2. Rh5) is curtly bilked 1. ... Rg7!, and 1. ... Rxf7! deletes 1. Bxf7? (2. Rg6, Re6). 1. Be4! makes the desired mates cascade forth — 1. ... Rg7 2. Rh5, 1. ... f6 2. Rg6, and 1. ... f5 2. Re6. The hindmost 1. ... Ra8 moseys into 2. Rxa8.

325. V WILSON
Schach-Echo,
1970

#2

326. RAL
Original

#2

327. G MOTT-SMITH
Chess Review,
1942

#2

328. RAL
Original

#2

329. R A LINCOLN
Vercherny Magadan,
1998

#2

330. G MALEIKA
Schach aktuell,
1982

#2

331. L RICZU
Chess Life & Review,
1974

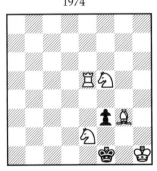

#2

332. H HULTBERG
Springaren,
1947

#2

333. R A LINCOLN
Newark Star-Ledger,
1996

#2

Maximums (cont'd)

In **325,** 1. Qd8+ creams a stranded king mid-board. Flights to the c-file result in 2. Rc3, and those to e-file are scuttled 1. Re7. Why all this massive armament? The avowed intention is to amplify checks. Initially, there are thirty available to White, most assuredly a miniature task record. Francis Vaux Wilson was an influential personality in the problem community. He dedicated many years to elaborating a systematic technique for mediation of any position's inherent worth. His protracted obsession with MOE (Method of Evaluation) was not widely shared by others. It was used sparingly by tourney arbiters. MOE, like predecessors, could not specify and rate the intangible — that wispy essence which secretes ingenuity and artistry.

Six distinct post-key mates may be connived in differing milieus. **326** has 1. Qd6? (2. Qf4) signal pragmatic enclosure which embargoes Black king use of e5. But a doughty bishop twits the offense, 1. ... Be5! 1. Qf2!, again espying f4, dexterously turns the tables. Now 1. ... Be5 blocks for 2. Qf3. Three more defenses allow White to gobble up that e5 square in transit — 1. ... Bh6 2. Qd4, 1. ... Se2 2. Qxe2, and 1. ... Sd3 2. Re2. Finally, 2. Qf5 overtakes 1. ... Ke5.

327 is rife with duals. Just one of several choices at White's disposal is mentioned. 1. Sf2 girdles the wistful Black queen in a delirious fog. Variants are 1. ... Qxf2 2. Bf7, 1. ... Qh2 2. Sg4, 1. ... Qg2 2. Qh4, 1. ... Qb8+ 2. Be8, 1. ... Qg5 2. Qg7, and 1. ... Qxg6+ 2. Qxg6. The multiples should be considered but picayune transgressions in this lusty six-gun shoot-out.

In **328,** White can fondle that juicy Black rook by 1. Qb3? (2. Qxa2), but is brushed off, 1. ... Ra1! A cold-blooded 1. Qb2! succeeds with 1. ... Ra1 2. Qxa1, 1. ... Ra3 2. Qxa3, 1. ... Ra4 2. Rxa4, 1. ... Ra5 2. Qb7, and 1. ... Sb5 2. Qxb5.

One last "six-bagger" also persecutes a dazed rook. **329** has to depend on the fretful 1. Qh4 (2. Qh7) for a key. Still, there is due compensation through some amiable conduits — 1. ... R~ 2. Be4, 1. ... Rg4 2. Qxg4, 1. ... Rh5 2. Qf6, 1. ... Rf5 2. Qh6, and 1. ... Kf5 2. Qe4. I would use flight-takers to wrench such a frenetic rumpus any day of the week.

330 is characterized by a bristling surfeit of solutions. Each line pacifies with alloting egress. The prostrate king must pad into the radii of star-flight. 1. Qh1 Kg3 2. Be1. 1. Bc1 Ke1 2. Qg1. 1. Qh3 Kg1 2. Be3. 1. Bc3 Ke3 2. Qg3. Queen and dark-squared bishop toss the hot potato in a game of "I'll move if you mate."

Minors Only

Here is an aggregate of nine positions without queen or rook. The lesser lights perform their duties in a piquant manner that glibly eschews those big galoots. **331** has 1. ... fxe2 2. Se3 swaddled away. 1. Bh4 makes room for another "White interference" by sidekick knight — 1. ... f2 2. Seg3.

A diaphanous **332** has both stumps of Black's b-pawn in the eagle's talons — 1. ... b6 2. Sc7 and 1. ... b5 2. Bc8. The dithering king cannot bluster into a mating zone, e.g. 1. Kc7? b6! and 1. Kc8? b5! The apposite 1. Ka8! steers clear of any contretemps.

333 has no tries, but the pawn patsy gets hornswoggled thrice. 1. Bf5 weaves a spider's web for 1. ... g6 2. Bg4, 1. ... g5 2. Sef6, and 1. ... gxh6 2. Sgf6. It was a lucky accident of construction getting that knight on e4 to prevent lower dips by the bishop.

334. Y CHEYLAN
The Problemist,
1985

#2   Two solutions

335. R A LINCOLN
Chess Life,
1999

#2

336. R A LINCOLN
Europe Echecs,
1996

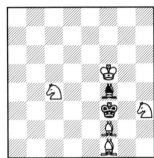

#2

337. M MCDOWELL
The Problemist,
1987

#2

338. RAL
Original

#2   Turn 90º clockwise

339. F SPRENGER
Chess Review,
1936

#2

340. G OHLERICH & H SUWE
The Problemist, 1987

#2

341. M MCDOWELL
The Problemist,
1990

#2

342. RAL
Original

#2

MINORS ONLY (CONT'D)

Despite promotions, **334** nevertheless qualifies for this section. Two "get-out-of-jail-free" cards are used conducting Black's anguished king on journeys into the abyss. 1. Kg4 decoys him to come forward 1. ... Kg6 2. f8=S and 1. f8=B suckers him to backpedal 1. ... Kg8 2. Sf6.

White has a yawning (2. Bxb3) in **335** when that f-pawn weighs anchor. However, all units are stuck like cockroaches in amber. 1. Bh7? (2. Bb1) seems level-headed, but is arrested 1. ... f5! Deserting the b3 blow, 1. Sc2! introduces (2. Sb4), where 1. ... bxc2 is battered 2. Bxf7. This block-threat has the clandestine g-bishop involved with set, virtual, and actual mates.

The slightly cockeyed burlesque of **336** gets by without pawns. Black's bishop must forgo his simultaneous guard over 2. S(x)d2 and 2. S(x)e5. No "waiter" beckons, so 1. Bh4? proposes (2. Sg1) only to be cut off at the knees, 1. ... Bg3! The rightful 1. Be1! carries the same threat. Namby-pamby defenses permit a set mate, 1. ... Be3 2. Se5, and a new one, 1. ... Bh2 2. Sg5.

The taut constrictions of **337** portend the indelible lineaments of a mutate. Both trustees are going to sell out his lordship by 1. ... S~ 2. B(x)c2 or 1. ... b4 2. Sc5. White rummages about madly for pinch-hitters. 1. Be2? S~ 2. B(x)d1, but 1. ... Sc2! 1. Bg6? b4 2. Be8, but 1. ... Sf5! The genteel 1. Be4! keeps watch on c2 while spanking 1. ... b4 2. Bc6.

338 uses a tawdry wedge, 1. Se4, to stop that pawn stone dead in his tracks. Black's jittery drudge must give up either 2. S(x)c5 or 2. S(x)c3. The right angle gyre has the vagrant moving in another direction. Henceforth, 1. Sd4 pinions to baffle the bishop by 2. S(x)c2 or 2. S(x)f3.

The lean layout of **339** is only the second example I have seen where minor pieces administer a star-flight. The key 1. Sd2, is letter perfect, forking over two rabbit warrens. The gracious finales smack of ambrosial nectar — 1. ... Ka1 2. Bd4, 1. ... Ka3 2. Sc4, 1. ... Kc3 2. Sa4, and 1. ... Kc1 2. Sd3. This superb success might have received proper recognition if submitted to a regular chess problem forum or theme tournament. The non-specialty publications presumably give "informal" awards, but are frequently negligent in doing so.

MIRROR MATES

This phenomenon was referred to in the prior # 281. I have long wondered about the sheer effrontery of **340**. 1. Kb7 wrests two cubicles for a vulgar swindle (2. Qg5). Okay, there's "ideal mirror mate" after 1. ... Kb5, but what do these authors have in mind? Beats me.

341 may also appear inane. 1. Rd8 threatens (2. Rxd7), which doesn't really happen as such. 1. ... Kd3 or 1. ... Kd1 revamp the configuration imperceptibly. 1. ... d6 and 1. ... d5 cause the rook to land on different squares, *i.e.* 2. Rxd6 and 2. Rxd5. The subtle lesson is that five distinct ideal mirror mates (including the "spoof" threat) can be shown with only five men. This zany notion has to be admired.

White must grapple with two rifts in **342**. 1. Sh6? shutters the f5 gateway menacing (2. Qf7), but 1. ... Kd5! 1. Sgf6? dams up d5 for (2. Qd7), but 1. ... Kf5! A prudent 1. Sf2! wins by vacating the premises. That e4 restraint undergrids mirror mates 1. ... Kd5 2. Qd7 and 1. ... Kf5 2. Qf7. More on this threat/defense/ mate curlicue, (Hannelius theme), can be found in the chapter entitled "Reversal of Fortune. "

343. W SPECKMANN
Schach-Echo,
1940

#2

344. RAL
Original

#2

345. S KOVALEV
Smena,
1998

#2

346. A DIKUSAROV
Comm., Pershoveresen,
1993

#2

347. A DIKUSAROV
Comm., Pershoveresen,
1993

#2

348. H V TUXEN
Skakbladet,
1959

#2

349. RAL
Original

#2

350. N KASHEEV
Zvyazda,
1968

#2

351. W SPECKMANN
Chess Life,
1972

#2

MISTRESS OF THE BOARD

Whenever White's queen undertakes a siege operation without any assistance, Black's king always dwells near board's lip. The flight-taking 1. Kc4 in **343** is not larceny. 1. ... Kb5 2. Qd5 was set, and the gesture deeds over a4. These capture mates are confluent for this minikin posse. 1. ... b5+ 2. Qxb5, 1. ... Ra7 2. Qxa7, 1. ... Ra8 2. Qxa8, and 1. ... Ka4 2. Qxa6. For whatever reason, this position has been subsequently reproduced in either the same or similar dress by many composers. I am convinced that this sample is the earliest, by *sui generis* miniaturist, the honorable Dr. Werner Speckmann.

An unflagging queen attains four knocks quite differently in **344**. 1. Kb4 draws nigh for (2. Qa5). 1. ... Bb5 2. Qxb5 is certainly nothing to write home about. However, the pot boils when that nestled b-pawn plays merry andrew with 1. ... b6 2. Qc8 (self-block) and 1. ... b5 2. Qc6 (self-interference).

The checkmates of **345** are branded with stale flavor. Erroneous expeditions provide some helpful spice. On 1. Qxg3? (2. Qg4), Black hangs by the skin of his teeth, 1. ... g5! Another raid, 1. Qe3?, can be studiously ignored 1. ... g2! White comes up roses after 1. Qe1! g5 2. Qe8, 1. ... g3 2. Qh4, and 1. ... Kg5 2. Qe5.

Andrei Dikusarov cops two honors by lacing up a Black king who roosts in the corner. **346** has 1. Ka6, with an attendant (2. Qa7), joyfully aggravate the decrepit mooncalf. The trio of defenses returns satisfactory coin. 1. ... Bb7+ 2. Qxb7, 1. ... Bg1 2. Qd8, and 1. ... Bb8 2. Qxc6.

347 is probably more interesting as Black has three hoplites strain to save their plagued oligarch. A domineering 1. Qb3 (2. Qb1) refuses to be appeased through 1. ... c2 2. Qb2, 1. ... Bg6 2. Qxa4, or 1. ... Rb4 2. Qa3.

The Danish composer, Harry Tuxen, was one of the most accomplished miniaturists of his generation. Much of his stupendous œuvre represents a yardstick to which other problems may be compared. If there is any way to procure five mates from a sole queen, Tuxen would most assuredly find it. **348** is distinguished by that resplendent inauguration key, 1. Qe7 (2. Qxh7). One after another, the bulwarks crumble in this jubilant *tour de force*. 1. ... Bg7+ 2. Qxg7, 1. ... Bg6 2. Qf8, 1. ... Bg8 2. Qxe5, and 1. ... Kg8 2. Qe8.

NIETVELT THEME

This tactic features defensive self-pin, which means pinner (also threat piece), cannot proceed lest unpinning releases a spoiler. All examples have a foolhardy king strolling into the skewer. In **349**, Black laughs at 1. Kc1? (2. Qb2) a3! Therefore, 1. Be1! takes a swipe at (2. Qc3). After 1. ... Ka3, 2. Qc3? frees up 1. ... Bb3!, but 2. Rd3 profits from the bishop's plight.

A smaller White material investment pays larger dividends in **350**. Two miscues are 1. Qb4? (2. Qd2) c3! and 1. Qg7? (2. Qg3) Kd3! 1. Qh7! (2. Qh3) is the coign of vantage White needs for the pin mate 2. Rf3 against 1. ... Kd3. There comes a felicitous premium upon the self-block/open gate 1. ... d3 2. Qa7. That horizontal pawn canopy garnishes an idyllic setting.

The Black queen is the principal of **351**. Amusingly enough, she's already pinned. 1. Qe4 (2. Qa4) has 1. ... Ka8 unpin for 2. Qa4? Qa6! Yet again a rook is on station to exploit via 2. Ra3. A further bleak gasp, 1. ... R~, lets White nosh on 2. Qxb7. One rarely comes across a miniature aristocrat devoid of bishops and knights.

352. S KIRILLOV
1st Prize, *Pershoveresen*,
1993

#2

353. B PUSTOVOI
Omskaya pravda,
1972

#2

354. J RICE
2nd Comm., Paisley,
1995

#2

355. R T LEWIS
Atlantic Chess News,
1995

#2

356. A WESTER
The Hindu,
1970

#2

357. G MARIZ
US Problem Bulletin,
1987

#2 (b) After key of (a)

358. G KUKIN
Thèmes-64,
1995

#2 (b) After key of (a)

359. F HEALEY
Chess Monthly,
1866

#2

360. D SHIRE
The Independent,
1988

#2

OJANEN THEME

Multiple threats are usually gauged a sloppy malfeasance against codes of good taste. White's supposed to conceal insidious designs with unlikely keys. The Ojanen theme has the temerity to require three or more threats. An equal number of different mates betide. **352** goes 1. S4e6 (2. Sd8, Sd4, Qc5). None of this occurs as Black's d7 yokel diverts all the action elsewhere — 1. ... d6 2. Qb5, 1. ... d5 2. Qc7, and 1. ... dxe6 2. Be4. The last variant endorses the presence of that bottom-feeding denizen.

PAISLEY

The 1995 residential weekend for the British Chess Problem Society was held in Paisley, Scotland. A "quick" twomover competition stipulated: "White's key move threatens mate and grants two flights. When Black takes the first flight, White achieves a new mate. When Black takes the second flight, White mates by switchback. " The idea had been shown in **353**. 1. Qd6 (2. Qe7) Kd8 2. Qf8 and 1. ... 0-0-0 2. Qc7. Boris Pustovoi manufactured more than two hundred castling miniatures.

The deeply inventive **354** formulates a method poles apart. Here's *prima facie* evidence of what a skilled artiste can do under the gun. 1. Qe4 (2. Qg2) makes an unrealized threat. However, "thematic" replies follow those compulsory capture orifices, 1. ... Kxg3 2. c8=Q and 1. ... Kxh3 2. Qh4.

Another castler is indulged via **355**. Although completed too late for Paisley, this raises the ante considerably. A formidable try, 1.Qxd6? (2.Sc7), resounds where 1...Ra7 goes amiss to 2.Qb8. The animal stubbornly clings to life, 1...Rc8! 1.Qg7! (2.Qxg8) extinguishes 1...Sg~ 2.Q(x)e7. 1. ... 0-0-0 fetches the 2.Qc7 retort as in Pustovoi's precursor. 1...Kd8 occasions a new incident — 2.Qd7.

PERPETUUM MOBILE

There is a certain species of problem whereby the key swings pendulum-like across a traverse. Change may or may not be in the tea leaves. **356** has 2. Sc3 and 2. Sg3 raring to go against 1. ... d2 and 1. ... f2. 1. Rg1 simply lets matters stand. Had the rook began at g1, the only move would be 1. Rc1 — "perpetual motion." Some observers will tactfully squabble with these do-nothing affairs. But such bantam creatures are deucedly tough to get aright, especially in the absence of White queen.

A pair of orderly changes occur in the willowy **357**. Set mates arrive beneath Black's king — 1. ... S~ 2. Q(x)c3 and 1. ... e5 2. Qd3. 1. Qg5 has post-key blows ascend above with 1. ... S~ 2. Q(x)c5 and 1. ... e5 2. Qd8. Obviously, part (b) drops back 1. Qg3, which merely emphasizes original conditions.

358 has the White king bobbing to and fro like a ping-pong ball. 1. Kb2 holds the fort to continue 1. ... b4 2. Qxd7 and 1. ... Kb4 2. Qd4. The second phase has 1. Ka2 do the same. Strangely, there is real substance behind this puny piffle. 1. Qd4? allows 1. ... b4!, while 1. Qxd7? sees 1. ... Kb4! go a glimmering. Tries and refutations, juxtaposed with actual play, form a Banny theme.

PINS GALORE

Composers have great joy explicating pinning tactics. The antiquated **359** has Black go from frying pan into fire after 1. Rd8. 1. ... Kd3 unpins the rook to be pinned anew from a discovery 2. Sc5.

White must pin the buccaneer rook of **360** 1. Rxe2? (2. Re1) leads to zilch, since 1. ... Re6! 1. Rf7? (2. Rxf6) heeds 1. ... e1=Q 2. Qxe1, but 1. ... Rf2! 1. Qf7! (2. Qxf6) will peg the chump somewhere along f-file and 2. Rxe1 guts 1. ... e1=Q.

361. H HULTBERG
Sydsvenska Dagbladet,
1928

#2

362. RAL
Original

#2

363. V KRIZHANOVSKY
The Problemist,
1992

#2

364. C S KIPPING
The Problemist,
1930

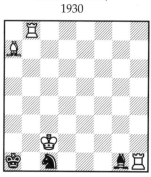

#2

365. V CHEPIZHNY
1st Prize, Nikolaev-200,
1989

#2

366. G YACOUBIAN
Tribune de Genève,
1979

#2

367. R A LINCOLN
The Problemist Supplement,
1998

#2

368. C MANSFIELD
Bournemouth Evening Echo,
1961

#2

369. RAL
Original

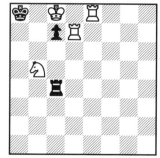

#2

PINS GALORE (CONT'D)

There's an ingrained aura of mutate anent **361.** Black's bishop both pins and is pinned. "How to solve" handbooks teach novices to unpin adversaries given ripe opportunity. 1. Qc4 is indeed the prescribed panacea. 1. ... d6 2. Qc6 is unaffected, but the liberated cleric loses his miter — 1. ... B~ 2. Sc6 and 1. ... Bxb4+ 2. Qxb4. Unpin of White's knight is a luscious sugarplum in this two-added mates covenant. Herbert Hultberg was the doyen of Sweden's problem domain. Author of six books, he founded and edited *Springaren.*

362 has an offside dobbin snorting in his reins. A logical 1. Se8? (2. Qg7), is thwarted by unpin 1. ... e6!, which also frees the rook to safeguard a simmering 2. Sf6? Paradoxically, unpinning directly with no threat, 1. Se6!, decides. 1. ... R~ costs 2. Q(x)g7 and 2. Qf8 whips 1. ... Rh7.

Two Black self-pins by capture are practically non-existent in miniature. **363** has a comic farce, 1. Qg7? (2. Qg4) 1. ... Se5 2. Qg3, but 1. ... Sg5! So 1. Qe2! goes seeking (2. Qf1). Removals on h2 would lay bare g3. Voraciously, the lynx-eyed queen growls at their sudden predicament — 1. ... Bxh2 2. Qxf3 and 1. ... Sxh2 2. Qg4.

Half-pin is a most difficult strategem to achieve in miniature. **364** shows the accessories after 1. Ra8 (2. Bd4). On moves such as 1. ... Bxa7 2. Rxa7 or 1. ... Bb6 2. Bxb6, the mate is operative because Black cannot interpose 2. ... Sa2? However, an immediate 1. ... Sa2 permits 2. Bd4 to ensue with no 2. ... Bxd4?, as bishop is now impaled. The additional pin on knight averting 2. ... Sc3? imbues a romantic problemistic rhapsody.

The natural correlation is White half-pin, when two offensive units are transfixed by withdrawal. **365** uses a diagonal skewer to temporarily disable White's remaining weapon. 1. Rd1? (2. Qxb1) would have a gorgeous interference unpin for 1. ... e4 2. Qa6, except 1. ... Ka2! Hence, 1. Qg1! parachutes down leaving her rook partner in the lurch. But he complacently cruises on 1. ... e4 2. Ra3. 2. Qa7 ties up the other loose end, 1. ... Ka2. Pinning of Black's bishop in try and key may seem a trifle strong, but should be excusable with these pertinent tactics.

The oft-quoted **366** needs only six men. Here, Black's pinner is already in the hot seat. White must marshal one of his rooks away from the vertical pin line. Which one to insulate makes an absorbing study. 1. Rg5? comes up shy after 1. ... Ka2!, since 2. Qa8+? unpins 2. ... Qh7! 1. Rg6! (2. Qh8) pre-blocks that succor, where Black queen wriggles prevent the threat only to unfasten 2. Rh5.

367 has nothing pinned initially. But there is rumbling beyond the mountains upon 1. Se5? (2. Qg8). 1. ... Qa6! flashes into view with a deadly pin. Hence, White must rely on the circumspect 1. Sb6! to obviate this resource. With g8 mate again on the bill of fare, Black can leapfrog 1. ... Qa2. No pin this time, so 2. Qc8. Diversions are roughly abused; 1. ... Kd8 2. Qd7 and 1. ... Kf8 2. Qf7.

White tingles over the prospect of 1. ... b1=S 2. Qg8 in **368.** But 1. ... b1=Q will have the queen glaring at a pin. Once more, "anticipatory" unpin is the soothing theriac against the serpent's fangs. 1. Kg2? musses up the road to g8, 1. ... b1=S! 1. Kh2! gets plaudits where 2. Qa7 outflanks 1. ... b1=Q.

The next two show other kinds of White self-pin. **369** has 1. Rxc7 (2. Kd7) awaken those hibernating rooks. The martyred fellow is resuscitated through 1. ... Rd4 2. Ra7. Obviously, 1. ... Rxc7+ is no fear since 2. Kxc7.

370. RAL
Original

#2

371. F PALATZ
Skakbladet,
1940

#2

372. B ZHEZHERUN
2nd Comm., *Smena,*
1997

#2   (b) Rg7>g6

373. R A LINCOLN
The Problemist,
1999

#2   Two solutions

374. C P SYDENHAM
Due Alfieri,
1980

#2   Two solutions

375. V PILCHENKO
2nd Prize, *Molodezhnaya gazeta,* 1993

#2   Ke2>b4

376. RAL
Original

#2   Three solutions

377. RAL
Original

#2

378. R A LINCOLN
Australian Chess Problem Magazine, 1997

#2

PINS GALORE (CONT'D)

370 has thrust and parry enliven the White king intrusions. 1. Ka6?, with double threats (2. Ra7, Rxb8), looks like a cocksure clincher. But there's a bee in the bonnet, 1. ... Bc8! Ironically, self-pinning 1. Kb6! (2. Rxb8) works just fine. Then, Black can unpin 1. ... R~ 2. Ra7 or take his nemesis 1. ... Rxb7+ 2. cxb7.

PRISON BREAKS

Stalemate relief may seem a mundane topic. Of course Black has to be given a move. Nonetheless, there are aesthetic ways of doing so. **371** quickens the pulse with a munificent 1. Rb2. Threats (2. Rxb1, Qxb1) are nugatory as 1. ... Kxb2 obliges a long-legged stretch 2. Qh8. One variation only, but this is the kind of position that persists in the memory.

Two rotten apples are flung before Black's king in **372.** First comes 1. Bf1, breaching a corridor for 2. Qb1 after 1. ... Kxf1. With rook displaced, 1. Sf2 plotzes for 1. ... Kxf2 2. Qa7. One line has queen moving diagonally to mate on rank. The other has her going along the rank to mate on a diagonal.

373 inveigles paired solutions without twinning. 1. Bb3 unglues the g3 caterpillar for 1. ... g2 whence 2. Be6 discovers and pins simultaneously. Then, 1. Rf3 self-destructs for 1. ... gxf3 2. Be6. This was composed for a "Happy New Year" edition of *The Problemist* which features originals with some humorous overtone. My little jibe was different first moves, but same mating rejoinders.

Colin Sydenham is that cordial Englishman who regales his problem audience with fiendish machinations of "duplex." Both sides are help-mated in turn. **374** is the only orthodox miniature I have seen by this composer, and it's a beaut. Black's access to a6 is permitted in two different ways. A hasty 1. Rh7+? fails because 1. ... Ka6! is cushioned from 2. Sc7+? or 2. Bb7+? interfering for 2. ... Ka7! 1. Sb6! (2. Sc8) functions as a direct battery after 1. ... Ka6. The second self-obstruction, 1. Bd6!, stutter-steps to allow 1. ... Ka6. Then the bishop resumes his jaunt with 2. Bb8.

White Grimshaw is a favored device to lift stalemate. **375** has 1. Bc4 shut off the rook compelling 1. ... Kc2 or 1. ... Kc1. The line is reopened as bishop proceeds to 2. Ba2. Part (b) has 1. Rc4 hesitate before continuing on to 2. Rc1 trampling 1. ... Ka2.

My **376** contains a mutual tie-up on c2. 1. Rc2 Ke4 2. Rd2 and 1. Bc2 Kc4 2. Be4 issue quite conformably. The third key disconcerts with a threat, 1. Qf6 (2. Qe5). That groveling goon must dejectedly rest on the scaffold as his b-pawn has been decreed a "prison break."

QUANTUM QUINTETS

The following fourteen problems are collected for their five post-key mates. Plentiful variety is generally always a cachet of successful miniatures. I must get this insufferable **377** off my chest. 1. Qa4 (2. Qc6) is a preposterous start. And I tried every which way but loose in finding a seemly initiative. Black clerical monkeyshines were worth the ordeal. 1. ... Bg2 2. Qg4, 1. ... Bd7 2. Qa6, 1. ... Bg3 2. Qe8, and 1. ... Bd8 2. Sd6.

There's no warm fuzzy feeling about **378** either. White's rook is pulled to b3 like a magnet for unprovided flights. 1. Rb3 lays the groundwork so that an enthusiastic queen carouses — 1. ... Kc4 (or 1. ... Kd4) 2. Qd3, 1. ... Kc6 2. Qb7, 1. ... Ke6 2. Qf5, 1. ... S~ 2. Q(x)e4, and 1. ... c4 2. Qd7.

379. W SPECKMANN
Dortmunder General-Anzeiger,
1931

#2

380. R A LINCOLN
Chess Life,
1997

#2

381. R A LINCOLN
Smena,
1996

#2

382. I ANDERSEN
1st Prize, *Skakbladet,*
1941

#2

383. R A LINCOLN
StrateGems,
1999

#2

384. R A LINCOLN
StrateGems,
1999

#2

385. V KOZHAKIN
2nd Prize, *Baltiskie shakhmaty,* 1991

#2

386. R A LINCOLN
The Problemist Supplement,
1992

#2

387. T SIERS
Hannoverscher Kurier,
1930

#2

QUANTUM QUINTETS (CONT'D)

A maestro ignites fiery conflagration for **379,** his first published two-mover miniature. The rugged attempt 1. Rb6? (2. Ra6, Qe1) goes badly awry to 1. ... Sc6! 1. Qb3! feeds Black's whole tribe into a whirling buzz saw — 1. ... S8~ 2. Q(x)b6, 1. ... S7~ 2. Q(x)b5,1. ... a3 2. Qxa3, 1. ... axb3 2. Ra1, and 1. ... Ka6 2. Qxa4.

380 must abide with a lackluster 1. Bc3 (2. b5) to get those blades turning. There is some merit in the spread of four defenses, each committing separate "mistakes. " 1. ... Sc6 2. Qxc6 (unguard), 1. ... Sb5 2. Qb3 (self-block), 1. ... Bd6 2. Qa6 (loss of line control), and 1. ... Ba5 2. Bxa5 (self-injury).

Activating that dozing castle would seem germane for **381.** 1. Ra5? yearns for 1. ... S~ 2. Rxd5, but 1. ... d4! 1. Qf4! is the *deus ex machina* that makes the pawn/rook battery bubble. There's a threat (2. b4) plus 1. ... Sa4 2. bxa4 or 1. ... Sc4 2. bxc4. Two more lollipops are 1. ... d4 2. Qf3 and 1. ... Kc3 2. Qd2.

For me, **382** is a garden of earthly delights. The actors are bunked in close propinquity resembling a stylized arrowhead pointing leftward. 1. Sc3 (2. Sb5) vexes Black's knight into general error with two emendatory self-blocks 1. ... S~ 2. e3, 1. ... Se3 2. Qf6, and 1. ... Se5 2. Qb6. The bishop also has a role by 1. ... Bxe2 (or 1. ... Be4) 2. Q(x)e4.

An ever-reliable y-flight admits some explicable tries in **383.** All prongs of the "y" are under scrutiny — 1. ... Kh7 2. Qf5, 1. ... Kh5 2. Qg4, and 1. ... Kf6 2. Rc6. 1. Ke4? (2. Qf5) cannot reckon with 1. ... B~! 1. Rb8? clips the wings of that butterfly, but 1. ... Kf6! A patient 1. Rc7! has the answers. One set mate changes for 1. ... Kh7 2. Qxg7. Black's peevish bishop acquiesces in 2. Qf7 on random moves. A corrective deterrent, 1. ... Bf6, boomerangs to 2. Qh7.

In **384,** a darling scam comes about. A White vedette quits his guard post and wanders off to never-never land. The introductory 1. Kf8? would ruffle 1. ... d6 2. Qe7, but cannot temper 1. ... f5! 1. Sd3! is not a fool's rush to oblivion as Black is now bound hand and foot. 1. ... d6 2. Qf7, 1. ... d5 2. Sc5, 1. ... f5 2. Qe5, 1. ... Ke7 2. Re4, and 1. ... Kd5 2. Qxd7.

Vladimir Kozhakin labors diligently to foster chess problem interest. His monthly pamphlet, *Kudesnik,* contains a treasury of original miniatures, cartoons, tourney results, announcements, and other assorted items. He also conducts regular columns for newspapers in his home town of Magadan, Russia. In my opinion, **385** ranks among his best efforts. Two blips on the radar screen are 1. Qb6? (2. Qa6) Bc7! and 1. Qd2? (2. Qb4, Qa2) Ka3 2. Qa5, but 1. ... Bd6! A glitzy flight-giver 1. Qd5! (2. Qa2) disentangles. Then, an instinctive 2. Qa8 outsmarts the bishop's save, 1. ... Bd6. A bouquet of honeyed branches has 1. ... b4 2. Ra1, 1. ... Ka3 2. Qb3, and 1. ... Ka5 2. Qxb5.

A five-car convoy chugs forth in **386.** Ordinarily, any flight-giving key with these miscellaneous mates would prove satisfying. But somehow this program is lacking in that winning panache. After 1. Qe3 (2. Qc5), the byplay runs 1. ... d2 2. Qb3, 1. ... Rc8 2. Qd4, 1. ... Kc3 2. Qc1, and 1. ... Kd5 2. Qe6. It all appears rather wishy-washy.

Four defenses don't faze the obstinate White queen of **387.** 1. Qg4 (2. Qd4) decimates 1. ... c5 2. Qe4, 1. ... e5 2. Qc4, 1. ... Sc6 2. Rb5, and 1. ... Se6 2. Qf5. Could anyone argue against this petite picnic? Well, some gloomy Gus would probably disparage the tacit symmetry. Regardless, I think two interferences on pawns which themselves self-block are super.

388. RAL
Original

#2

389. R A LINCOLN
The Problemist, 1990

#2

390. R A LINCOLN
Smena, 1996

#2

391. M LOKKER
Pajtas, 1967

#2

392. V KRIZHANOVSKY
The Problemist, 1995

#2

393. M MCDOWELL
Ideal-Mate Review, 1987

#2

394. J R NEUKOMM
Pajtas,
1947

#2

395. V CHEPIZHNY
Chess Life,
1969

#2 Two solutions

396. V DYACHUK &
S VESELENCHUK
5th HM., *StrateGems*, 1998

#2 (b) Remove Bf7

QUANTUM QUINTETS (CONT'D)

Castling is a dependable implement for multifarious purposes. The first four mates of **388** are somewhat trite — 1. Qb7 (2. Qxc8) S~ 2. Q(x)e7, 1. ... Kd8 2. Qd7, and 1. ... Kf8 2. Qf7. Thank goodness for 1. ... O-O 2. Qh7 adducing some glamour.

Flight-giving key with varied conflict —'tis a consummation devoutly to be wished. **389** has just this with 1. Qb4 (2. Qe4) battling off 1. ... Sc5 2. Qxc5, 1. ... Sd6 2. Qxd6, 1. ... e5 2. Qc4, and 1. ... Kc6 2. Qxb7.

White's queen recruits but a single coadjutor in **390.** An unassuming 1. Qc3 (2. Qa1) shellshocks the opposing covey. Black's mishmash of defenses wilts under the hard onslaught. 1. ... Se7 2. Qa5, 1. ... Sb4 2. Qxb4, 1. ... Bb1 2. Qxc6, and 1. ... b2 2. Qa3. "Arrival" effects of the knight have dual avoidance, *i.e.* 1. ... Sb4, not 2. Qa5?, and 1. ... Se7, not 2. Qb4?

RADICAL DEPARTURES

These seven problems were chosen for their mercurial nature. Final positions are a far cry from the nidus. This convincingly verifies that an awful lot of commotion takes place in two moves. Mind-boggling turnabouts have a special attraction for those beginners who might suppose miniature strategy is arid. None boost the commodious mate catalogs of the previous subdivision, but all have exciting surprises that are deluxe. In **391,** White's imposing array metes out 1. ... S6~ 2. Q(x)d5 and 1. ... S1~ 2. Q(x)c3, but is strapped for moves. Queen and rook must remain stock-still and knight marauding is outlawed *e.g.* 1. Se6? (2. Qc5, Qb5, Qd4) Sc3+! With 1. ... Sa4+! ridiculing 1. Kb2?, pickings have decreased to nil. There is, however, sound resolution by 1. Sa6! (2. Qc5, Qd4), which meticulously revises 1. ... Sc3+ to 2. Rxc3. This is a kind of mongrel block threat with double attack.

392 makes a looming 1. ... e5+! the cardinal priority. 1. Ke5? gets cautiously out of harm's way. Now the hagridden Black king faces 1. ... Kg2 2. Qf1, 1. ... Ke3 2. Rh3, and 1. ... Kg4 2. Qe2, but 1. ... e6! 1. Qe6! blocks that nuisance completely. This slues a fundamental realignment with 1. ... Kg2 2. Qh3, 1. ... Kf4 2. Rf1, and 1. ... Ke2 2. Qg4. Naysayers ruthlessly excoriate such unprovided checks. My vote goes for the sweeping changes.

An "ideal mirror mate" is prepared for **393.** 1. ... Ke5 permits 2. Re8 and that's that. But White cannot burn a tempo. Henceforth, 1. Rd3 nosedives for 1. ... Ke5 2. Re3, again with ideal mirror mate. McDowell's placements might be the only possible rendering of this shipshape reversal.

Another intimidated sweat hog flees from White's fury in **394.** Surely, there are means of maintaining 1. ... Kf4 2. Qg4 and 1. ... Kxf6 2. Qf7. Try as one may, everything except 1. Qa2 upsets the predisposition. Then 1. ... Kf4 is undermined 2. Qf2.

395 will make the skeptic a believer in two solutions. 1. Qa8 promptly buries 1. ... Kg1 2. Qg2 and 1. ... Kxe3 2. Qf3. Then, 1. Qa6 gaffs the writhing fish by 1. ... Kg1 2. Qf1 and 1. ... Kxe3 2. Qe2. The coordinated mates frame a white square nimbus around the Black king. Viktor Chepizhny edits the problem pages of *Smena*, a Moscow-based magazine.

396 has the most thorough alterations to y-flight one is apt to see. White starts with a thunderclap 1. c4+ shoveling the king to 1. ... Ke6 2. Bh3, 1. ... Ke4 2. Qf4, and 1. ... Kc5 2. Qe7. Expunging the Black bishop forces 1. Kc7, baiting the trap for 1. ... Ke6 2. Bc4, 1. ... Ke4 2. Bg2, and 1. ... Kc5 2. Bc3. The second round doesn't have anything remotely like that of part (a).

397. V MARKOVSKY
Probleemblad,
1997

#2 (b) Re4>e2

398. N PLAKSIN
Shakhmaty v. SSSR,
1973

#2

399. M SCHLOSSER
5th Comm., *Thèmes-64,*
1980

#2

400. V ZHELTONOZHKO
Probleemblad,
1996

#2

401. S LOYD
St. Louis Democrat,
1907

#2

402. N SHANKAR RAM
1st Comm., *The Problemist,*
1981

#2

403. M LIPTON
Problemisten,
1965

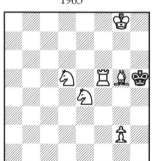

#2

404. RAL
Original

#2

405. V MARKOVSKY
Probleemblad,
1996

#2

RADICAL DEPARTURES (CONT'D)

Twinning, by its very essence, drums up radical departure. **397** has a set 1. ... f5 2. Re6, but coping with 1. ... fxg5! takes some doing. The brilliant 1. Bf8 reacts to 1. ... fxg5 with a mate transference 2. Re6. 1. ... f5 changes to 2. Qh6, plus an added wrinkle, 2. Qg4, is pursuant on 1. ... Kxg5. Part (b) has White's rook go two paces backward to begin 1. Rh2. New clientele are 1. ... f5 2. Qh5 and 1. ... fxg5 2. Qd3.

RETROGRADE ANALYSIS

This subject is usually considered as "fairy chess." I have refrained from including any of this genre within. But **398** is eligible as a normal setting. One only has to determine Black's last move to make 1. d8=R Kxc7 2. Rd7 plausible. Remove the White rook, place the Black king at b8, and put a Black knight on b6. Finally, lay a White pawn upon b7. The preceding play went 1. ... Sa8 2. bxa8=R+ Kb7 and the diagram bursts into sight!

REVERSAL OF FORTUNE

Throughout the past several decades, two-mover composers have been fixated with "reversal" themes. Paradoxical elements multiply among tries, threats, defenses, and mates. These bread and butter issues find flourishing elucidation in miniature. The Banny theme traces out this series: 1. A? x! 1. B? y! Key! 1. ... x 2. B and 1. ... y 2. A. **399** has fraudulent red herrings 1. Kb3? (2. Bf6) Rxh7! and 1. Kc2? (2. Bf6) Rxg8! Following 1. Bf6! (2. K~), Black must *nolens volens* return the tries 1. ... Rxg8 2. Kb3 and 1. ... Rxh7 2. Kc2.

The opulent **400** is destined for future anthologies. Here is found an utterly breathtaking tripartite cycle. A constant (2. Bf8) is posed during virtual phases. 1.

Sc6? Kd6! 1. Sd5? Kd4! 1. Sf5? Kb4! Following the key 1. Bf8! those tries must restart after 1. ... Kd6 2. Sd5 (holding c7), 1. ... Kd4 2. Sf5 (protecting the rook), and 1. ... Kb4 2. Sc6 (guarding a5).

The Dombrovskis theme is defined by this alphabetic mumbo-jumbo: 1. ? (2. A) x! 2.? (2. B) y! 1. Key! 1. ... x 2. A and 1. ... y 2. B. Loyd knew nothing of these matters in 1907. But he executed the majestic **401** undoubtedly oblivious of a try/defense/mate pattern. 1. Rb1? (2. Bf7) Ke6! 1. Ke5? (2. Bd3) Kb5! 1. Ra6! condemns the pitiable Black king to be harpooned 1. ... Ke6 2. Bf7 or 1. ... Kb5 2. Bd3.

Nearly seventy-five years later, the Dombrovskis machinery is running full tilt. An Indian maven gets awarded for an interesting schema with orthogonal flights. **402** shows 1. Rb3? (2. Qd3) Kd5! 1. Re1? (2. Qe4) Kxc4! 1. Rb6! Kd5 2. Qd3 and 1. ... Kxc4 2. Qe4. Note that otherwise goofy b-pawn is necessary for dispelling the unwanted 1. Qf5? b6!

Black escapes faltering feelers in **403** by grazing the vulnerable White rook — 1. Kf7? (2. Sf6) Kg4! 1. Sf2? (2. Sf4) Kg6! 1. Re5! snatches the cookie jar from the king's hungry grasp for 1. ... Kg4 2. Sf6 and 1. ... Kg6 2. Sf4.

My **404** uses a practically equivalent sketch, but there's an extra prize in the Cracker Jack box. 1. Kf6? (2. Bf3) Kg4! 1. Sf2? (2. Bf7) Kg6! 1. Sg5! pilots the proverbial tailpieces 1. ... Kg4 2. Bf3 and 1. ... Kg6 2. Bf7. Both finales are valued ideal mates.

The ultramodern **405** contains a post-key threat and a side variation. It's evident that ongoing investigations into the ever labyrinthine Dombrovskis will requite such enrichment. 1. Kb3? (2. Sc4) Ka6! 1. b8=S? (2. Qc5) Bf2 2. Bd2, but 1. ... Kb4! 1. Be3! (2. Qa4) Ka6 2. Sc4 and 1. ... Kb4 2. Qc5.

406. M LOKKER
Shakhmaty v SSSR,
1973

#2

407. V ZHELTONOZHKO
Comm., Probleemblad,
1990

#2

408. E SCHAPOVALOV
Revista Schach,
1972

#2

409. A SLESARENKO
Mat,
1986

#2

410. G MOSIASHVILI
Probleemblad,
1997

#2

411. L GROLMAN
Probleemblad,
1995

#2 (b) Bg5>h4

412. N PLETENEV
Shakhmaty Riga,
1985

#2

413. M BANASZEK
The Problemist,
1996

#2

414. V PILCHENKO
The Problemist,
1995

#2

REVERSAL OF FORTUNE (CONT'D)

The Hannelius theme is delineated by this blueprint: 1. ? (2. A) x! 1. ? (2. B) y! 1. Key! 1. ... x 2. B and 1. ... y 2. A. As will be seen, the solution may or may not threaten a new mate. For a problemist of Miklos Lokker's stature, this thorny postulate is a walk in the park. **406** has crisp tries recoil against Black's timely promotions — 1. Qg5? (2. Qg2) f1=Q! and 1. Qf4? (2. Qh2) f1=S! After 1. Qe2! (2. Qf1), that pawn defends by letting the a7 partisan through to g1, but 1. ... f1=Q 2. Qh2 or 1. ... f1=S 2. Qg2.

The White queen will get aid and comfort from her pilgrim bishop in **407.** How she gets it is anomalous. Head-on aggression peters out due to Black's debonair knight — 1. Bd4? (2. Qf2) Sh1! and 1. Bc3? (2. Qe1) Se2! A snuggling ambush 1. Bh4! douses former counters 1. ... Sh1 2. Qe1 and 1. ... Se2 2. Qf2. Only a dour spoilsport cavils with other knight moves allowing duals.

In **408,** there is a gnarly hybrid of Dombrovskis and Hannelius. 1. Ba5? (2. Qb6) Kd6! 1. Bb4? (2. Qc5) Kc7! 1. Bh4? Kd6 2. Qb6 or 1. ... Kc7 2. Qc5. This phase has a complete Dombrovskis paradigm, but does not solve as 1. ... b4! remains. So the bold, untiring wayfarer lights upon 1. Bf2! (2. Qb6,Qc5). Flights separate hostile intents by the Hannelius equation — 1. ... Kd6 2. Qc5 and 1. ... Kc7 2. Qd6. A double threat fails to detract from these wondrous marvels of finesse.

The le Grand theme is encrypted: 1. ? (2. A) x 2. B, but 1. ... y! 1. Key! (2. B) x (2. A). **409** shows this nucleus starkly by 1. Be2! (2. Qc4) Ke4 2. Qd3, 1. ... e4 2. Sf4, but 1. ... Ke6! 1. Kb6! (2. Qd3) Ke4 2. Qc4 and 1. ... e4 (or 1. ... Kd6) 2. Qc5. The roller coaster ride pleases, but one must bewail an execrable try refutation.

Another abominable rebuff debases the virtual phase of **410.** 1. Sd4? (2. Qb5) Kd3 2. Qe2, but 1. ... Kxc5! 1. Bb4! works with (2. Qe2) Kd3 2. Qb5. There is some amusement where try and key touch on the same locus. Also, mates bracket that gaunt scarecrow from opposite sides.

In **411,** the foe exults over carefree passage to c5, e5, and the entire sixth rank. Solution devolves on which start shall muzzle a smidgen of this extended immunity. 1. Bf4? (2. Qc4) has dominion over 1. ... Kc6 2. Qb5, but 1. ... Ke6! 1. Ke7! (2. Qb5) changes 1. ... Kc6 back to the spurious threat 2. Qc4. Part (b) will not succeed by 1. Ke7?, since 1. ... Ke5! Therefore, 1. Bg3! (2. Qc4) steps up to the plate with 1. ... Kc6 2. Qb5 or 1. ... Ke6 2. Qf7.

A junior progeny is called "pseudo le Grand." The same anatomy has differentiated Black responses invert threat and mate. **412** goes 1. Bd1? (2. Qf4) d2 2. Qf3, but 1. ... Kd2! The more politic 1. Se4! (2. Qd3) incarcerates 1. ... Kxe4 2. Qf4 and 1. ... Ke2 2. Qf2.

The Vladimirov theme is signified: 1. A? x! 1. B? y! 1. Key! 1. ... x 2. A and 1. ... y 2. B. **413** has a fivefold depiction and makes the whole shebang as easy as rolling off a log. 1. Rb3? (2. Ra3, Qg7) Rxb3! This process is echoed up the column ending with 1. Rb7? (2. Ra7, Qg7) Rxb7! After 1. Qg7! (2. Qa7), the tries slavishly subvert former defenses 1. . . Rb3 2. Rxb3, 1. . . Rb4 2. Rxb4, etc. Lastly, 2. Qxb2 crocodiles 1. ... Rxb2.

RUDENKO THEME

This enigmatic maze intermingles set mates, virtual and actual double threats, and changed play. **414** may either edify or confuse solvers. 1. Sc1? Ke4 2. Qe6, 1. ... Kc4 2. Qc6, but 1. ... f3! 1. Sed4? (2. Qe6, Qc6) 1. ... Ke4! 1. ... Kc4! 1. Sfd4! (2. Qe6, Qc6) retrieves 2. Qf5 and 2. Qb5 for 1. ... Ke4 and 1. ... Kc4.

415. V KOVALENKO
1st Prize, BJM60 Ty,
1997

#2

416. R A LINCOLN
Newark Star-Ledger,
1987

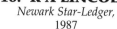

#2

417. M KORMILTSEV
Sp. Comm., Chepizhny JT,
1994

#2

418. R A LINCOLN
Comm., *Ideal-Mate Review,*
1998

#2

419. RAL
Original

#2

420. M VELUCCHI
A.R.P.A. Bulletin,
1994

#2

421. R A LINCOLN
Chess Life,
1998

#2

422. W MASSMANN
Schweizeische Schachzeitung,
1962

#2

423. M LIPTON
Sp. HM., *diagrammes,*
1997

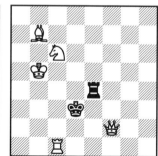

#2

RUKHLIS THEME

Ordinarily, this plot has two parts. First, set or virtual play gets at least two mates transferred post-key. Then, new mates arise for those defenses associated with the initial phase. **415** protracts a sequence over three go arounds. 1. Kc3? Ke4 2. Qf5, 1. ... Kc5 2. Qc6, but 1. ... Ke5! 1. Ke3? Kc4 2. Qb5, 1. ... Ke5 2. Qe6, but 1. ... Kc5! These tangents explain why that backward White pawn is berthed on d2. 1. c8=S! conveniently guards d6 to wind up 1. ... Ke5 2. Qf5 and 1. ... Kc5 2. Qb5. This formal contest toasted the birthdays of British composers Barry Barnes, John Rice, and Michael Lipton.

SHAPE

Placement of men on the board can be manipulated to produce quizzical and sometimes facetious patterns. **416** packs all participants into an elongated conga line. 1. Qg3 (2. Qd3) acquires five mates altogether — 1. ... f1=Q 2. Qe3, 1. ... f1=S 2. Qg2, 1. ... Kxd2 2. Qxf2, and 1. ... Kf1 2. Bd3. The fainéant h2 "watchman" ratifies White's threat.

417 takes on a contour emblematic of the letter "Y." 1. Rg6 transmogrifies the vista into a lopsided check mark after 1. ... Rxg6 2. Sxg6. Other finishes are 1. ... Rxf7 (or 1. ... Rg8) 2. R(x)g8 and 1. ... Rxh7+ 2. Rxh7.

Everything is tightly compacted into a Procrustean bed in **418.** This isosceles triangle has all the pieces expropriate f2 by 1. Rf2 Bxf2 2. Sxf2. The final result leaves a pair of spaced "pipes."

The Latin cross of **419** has no distinguishing property except its shape. Sets for 1. ... c5 2. Qb7 and 1. ... e5 2. Qf7 must give way. Moves such as 1. Qe8? would let the bishop run wild. The wanton pin is kept 1. Qd8! with more distant, albeit concurrent, mates servicing 1. ... c5 2. Qa8 or 1. ... e5 2. Qg8.

The sixth rank linkage displayed in **420** affects the initials of the sponsoring agency. This Italian theme tourney required a foursome of bishop, king, pawn, and bishop situated horizontally. Italian word equivalents for these units (alfiere, re, and pedone) spell out ARPA as shown. There's nothing to the play following a softly pedestrian 1. Bf8 when 1. ... S~ knuckles under to 2. B(x)g7.

SHARP FOCUS

Each succeeding example features a stressed Black piece trying to defend two points synchronously. The cornered queen of **421** controls smoldering strikes at 2. Be4 and 2. R2h6. White maintains these implanted pylons by using the only doable expedient, 1. Bg2. It's slightly unusual to have the key component traveling toward the "overworked" rival.

422 has Black's b5 schnook sagging under guard duties of b4 and e5. White possesses but one suitable doohickey accentuating this misfortune. 1. Bf1 stays nuzzled behind the knight who gaily gallops on 1. ... R~file 2. Se5 or 1. ... R~rank 2. Sb4. Attempts to meddle with the queen backfire by self-block — 1. ... Rb6 2. Qd7 and 1. ... Rb7 2. Qc5.

A comparable tapestry is stitched by **423.** Adding that White unit opens a floodgate of tries. 1. Rc2? (2. Qd2) is a fiasco owing to 1. ... Re3! The impulsive rook must also resile from 1. Rc5? since 1. ... Rc4! 1. Ka5? swoons to the blatant 1. ... Ra4+! On 1. Kb6?, Black yanks a none too obvious pin 1. ... Re6! out of the hat. 1. Bh8! brings blessed solace at last. The mating rigmarole apes Massmann's — 1. ... R~file 2. Sb4, 1. ... R~rank 2. Se5, 1. ... Re3 2. Qc2, and 1. ... Re2 2. Qd4. One big improvement has Black's rook going to both focal points with check, thereby preventing duals, *i.e.* 1. ... Rb4+ 2. Sxb4 and 1. ... Re5+ 2. Sxe5.

424. RAL
Original

#2

425. F LAZARD
L'Eclaireur du Soir,
1924

#2

426. RAL
Original

#2

427. A P da SILVA
Problemas,
1944

#2

428. M VUKCEVICH
Plain Dealer,
1970

#2

429. RAL
Original

#2

430. RAL
Original

#2

431. R KUJOTH
Milwaukee Journal,
1946

#2

432. A KARGAPOLOV
Cross-check,
1995

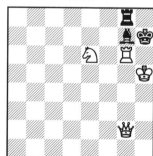

#2

SHARP FOCUS (CONT'D)

Dual avoidance figures in these last three entries. **424** uses check to White king and line-cut to ascertain unrepeated mates. 1. Sc8 fleeces Black's rook into 1. ... R~rank 2. Qe7 and 1. ... R~file 2. Sb6. Focal junctures are 1. ... Rb6+ 2. Sxb6 and 1. ... Re7 2. Qxe7. One further kumquat is 1. ... Re8 2. Qd6.

A real sleight of hand ennobles **425**. Presumably, the opposing stallions are huddled in their respective paddocks to halt immediate convulsions stemming from 1. Sd6+? or 1. Sg3+? The key 1. Se7 soars off depositing binate queen threats (2. Qd5,Qf5). Now, a seamless garment of eight Black moves guards one mating square or the other!

The avoidance mechanism is already in place for **426**. Black's queen stands atop the ramparts gamely surveying that maverick knight hell-bent upon 2. Sa5 or 2. Sd8. Arriving on the conflux observes the correlative mate becoming captive to 1. ... Qa5 2. Sxa5 and 1. ... Qd8 2. Sxd8. But there is a gleam of hope in one safe fallback — 1. ... Qxb7! White summarily eradicates that recourse with 1. Bd6 to continue 2. Qc5.

SHOWCASE FOR SOLVERS

Most modern problems are composed for the welfare of rapt analysts who idolize prickly pattern nuances. Such turmoil will often glaze over the eyes of some laymen. This section has a baker's dozen with no particular "thematic" rationale whatsoever. They are merely honest puzzles which should indulge the neglected average solver. **427** might hoodwink a few into thinking the c2 flight is a solemn anxiety. In truth, the philanthropic 1. Qh1 sheds e2 as well. A despondent Black depletes his sorry choices — 1. ... d4 2. Qe4, 1. ... Kc2 2. Qb1, 1. ... Ke2 2. Qf1, and 1. ... Kd4 2. Qxd5.

Another queen pitch to the basement corner is found in **428**. Here, the overriding urgency is to disenthrall that a8 legionnaire. 1. Qh1 gets an accolade by nice "model" mates 1. ... Kxa8 2. c7 and 1. ... Kxc8 2. Qh8. White's king actually has an important role by occupying that specific domicile. He keeps cooks such as 1. Qh7? at arm's length.

The rebel king of **429** is proud owner of radial fissures at g3, h3, f5, and h5. 1. Qc6 launches a heat-seeking missile of fearsome amplitude. Scruffy defenses are no match for White's intransigent queen — 1. ... Kh5 2. Qg6, 1. ... Kf5 2. Qe6, 1. ... Kg3 (or 1. ... Kh3) 2. Qg2, and 1. ... f3 2. Qxf3.

Under normal circumstances, I would not allow any problem of mine with but one pair of mates to be shown in public. Nonetheless, **430** is personally fulfilling. 1. Sg5+? fatally interferes on the queen's line of guard, 1. ... Kh6! A determined act of nonchalance takes 1. Qb6! to a foreign sector leaving h6 be. Then 1. ... B~ opens queen's vision to the flight square and 2. Sg5 happens after all. 1. ... Kh6 goes doddering into a mortal pin mate 2. Rh8. Cool beans.

Solvers must come to grips with 1. ... Ka1! in **431,** so crucial measures are needed. The unpinning gift key, 1. Qd4, is a pearl. Three closers have excellent appeal where each White piece registers a knockout — 1. ... Ka1 2. Rxc1, 1. ... Kxc2 2. Bh7, and 1. ... B~ 2. Qxb2.

432 is somewhat akin since White's total complement notches a checkmate. Another fervent queen excursion, 1. Qb2, institutes a pinning lineup for 1. ... Kh8 2. Rh6. The selfsame butts in for all bishop removals except 1. ... Bf8, when 2. Sg5 takes a laurel. One final matter is 1. ... R~ 2. Qxg7.

433. R A LINCOLN
The Problemist,
1992

#2

434. RAL
Original

#2

435. M LESCHEMELLE
4th Comm., *diagrammes,*
1996

#2

436. R A LINCOLN
Newark Star-Ledger,
1998

#2

437. W BARCLAY &
T SWEENEY
Beauty is Where You Find it, 1972

#2

438. RAL
Original

#2

439. F H SINGER
The Problemist,
1984

#2

440. DR K FABEL
Der Mitarbeiter,
1937

#2

441. R A LINCOLN
StrateGems,
1999

#2

SHOWCASE FOR SOLVERS (CONT'D)

White has a snug 2. Qe5 set for 1. ... f5 in **433**. An ephemeral phantasm is 1. Qc5? (2. Re7), which gets challenged by the gruesome 1. ... Sd5! That smart aleck knight is bamboozled by 1. Qb4!, when 1. ... S~ relents to 2. Q(x)e4. Flights are blitzed elatedly by 1. ... Kc4 2. Qc4 and 1. ... Kf5 2. Qg4, while 1. ... f5 changes to 2. Qd6.

The tries of **434** meet unexpectedly stiff defiance. Despite scrawny reserves, Black postpones his certain doom with keen bravado. A bluff threat 1. Qh3? (2. Sh~) is repulsed 1. ... g4! Waiters also cannot make a dent — 1. Kg7? gxh4! or 1. Qe5? Kg4! It takes 1. Qf6! to crack that durable carapace with 1. ... g4 2. Sf4, 1. ... gxh4 2. Qxh4, 1. ... Kg4 2. Qf3, and 1. ... Kh6 2. Qh8.

435 mixes and matches flights with reciprocal turnabouts. 1. Rf6? shepherds 1. ... Ke4 2. Qc4 and 1. ... Kd5 2. Qd3, but the king sprints 1. ... Kc3! 1. Se5! muscles in where one virtual mate becomes a threat (2. Qc4). This powerhouse will also be inflicted on any trips to c3 or d5. The other particle from the try phase, 2. Qd3, is now responsible for 1. ... Ke4.

In **436,** 1. ... Kh3! isn't much — it's all Black has. But those circling vultures must disengage a wider margin of amnesty to mollify that ticklish escape. The spruce 1. Sf1 bleeds a wobbly king on 1. ... Kh3 2. Qg3, 1. ... Kg1 (or 1. ... Kh1) 2. Sfe3, and 1. ... Kf3 2. Qe4.

The shadowy h7 pawn of **437** has two useful functions, although appearances are to the contrary. First, it disqualifies an overzealous 1. Kg4? (2. Qf3) because of 1. ... h5+! After 1. Sc3! (2. Sd5), 1. ... h6 is the sole move permitting White's threat. Other casualties are 1. ... d2 2. Qg3 and 1. ... Kf4 2. Qf2.

There is a brouhaha of tries in **438** which should test the mettle of solvers. A husky 1. Qd7? incorporates numerous threats, but shrivels on 1. ... g4! 1. Qd8? (2. Qf8) burgles that anterior district again, where 2. Qh3 defeats 1. ... g4, but 1. ... Bd6! or 1. ... Be5! suffice. 1. Bg4? aspires for (2. Qh3) directly, but 1. ... Bg3! The brawl ends when 1. Bh5! heaves a grapnel at Black's innards. Defenses to (2. Qxg6) return the notorious 2. Qh3 on 1. ... Kxh5 and 1. ... gxh5 opens a smooth glide path to 2. Qh7.

439 is a great sentimental favorite. Warring sighs and groans wouldn't give me a shred of clue how to proceed. Yes, 1. ... Kxf5 cringes at the advent of 2. Bh7, but any wee disruption upsets the fragile equipoise. A razzle-dazzle key, 1. Ree5, guards the en prise rook while becoming the sacrificial lamb for 1. ... fxe5. Then, 2. Bh7 mates anyway. Voilà!

STUMBLEBUMS

There are several problem types where Black is constantly getting in his own way. Mutual interference between rook and bishop is the most well-known. The pedigree belongs to a nineteenth century composer, Walter Grimshaw. **440** demands the precaution of lugging White's king off a limpid pin line. 1. Ke7 clamps Black into a fell vise with no mercy. The rook/bishop snarl goes off 1. ... Rg2 2. Qf1 or 1. ... Bg2 2. Qg3. Extraneous disasters are 1. ... Rf2 2. Qc3 and 1. ... Rxe2+ 2. Qxe2.

Chances for an original Grimshaw grow slimmer with the passing of time. **441** may be anticipated, but I have not seen it before. The no-nonsense 1. Kg3 (2. Bg4) defrauds Black into a scrunch on f5 — 1. ... Rf5 2. Be8 and 1. ... Bf5 2. Qf5. A palmy by-product is 1. ... Bg6 2. Qh4.

442. RAL
Original

#2

443. A STEPOCHKIN
Zog,
1987

#2

444. RAL
Original

#2

445. V VEDERS
Mini-Matt,
1971

#2

446. R A LINCOLN
Newark Star-Ledger,
1999

#2

447. RAL
Original

#2

448. R A LINCOLN
The Problemist,
1997

#2 (b) Bd6>e5

449. V PILCHENKO
1st-3rd Prize, *Smena,*
1992

#2

450. V PILCHENKO
2nd Prize, *Vpered,*
1991

#2

STUMBLEBUMS (CONT'D)

White must start checking in **442** with his king in peril. Three catchpenny tries feather the nest. 1. Qc6+? Rb5 2. Qxb5, but 1. ... Kb3! 1. Qc2+? Kb4 2. Qc4, but 1. ... Rb3! 1. b3+? Rxb3 2. Qa5, but 1. ... Ka3! There's one more shaft in the quiver, 1. Qc4+! Black's aggrieved personnel interpose to yield 1. ... Rb4 2. Qa2 and 1. ... Bb4 2. Qc2.

Interference between a bishop and pawn is known as pawn Grimshaw. It is also identified with the prepossessing sobriquet, "Pickabish." The pawn must be located on second rank so that the bishop stops a two-step advance. **443** begins with a probe, 1. Qb2? (2. Qxg7), which gets undone by a snappy line-cut, 1. ... g5! The fastidious 1. Kg8! (2. Qh7) causes an altercation on g6 with distant coups 1. ... g6 2. Qh1 and 1. ... Bg6 2. Qc1. 2. Sxf7 engorges a spite check, 1. ... Bf7+.

Learning of this position sent me leafing through the chaotic clutter I call a scrapbook. **444** was exhumed which contains a tincture of difference. One bland nibble is 1. Qg7? (2. Qxb7), warded off by 1. ... Bc7! 1. Kb8! (2. Qa7) gives the facsimile 1. ... Bb6 2. Qf1. But 1. ... b6 interferes behind the bishop rather than in front — 2. Sc7.

"Royal Grimshaw" describes mutual confusion between Black king and line-moving ally. The king impedes a guard line and the other unit self-blocks. The astonishing key of **445** leaves any mimetic impostors trailing in the dust. 1. Bb1 rolls out the carpet for thematic congestion on a3 — 1. ... Ra3 2. Qc2 and 1. ... Ka3 2. Qa2. 2. Qc2 also blissfully rebukes 1. ... Kxb1. Side desserts are 1. ... R~ 2. Qxb4 and 1. ... b3 2. Qc1.

446 invites the principals to mambo on h7. 1. Qf6 (2. Qf7) rejoices upon 1. ... Rh7 2. Qxf8 and 1. ... Kh7 2. Qh8. The flimsy 1. ... Bg7 is pocketed 2. Qxg7. This arrangement achieved the desired output of four mates. A serious disadvantage lies with that key piece under attack at the inception.

Two examples highlight a king and bishop getting too close for comfort. Both of Black's underlings protect their seigneur in **447** from 1. Qd8+? Bd6! or 1. Qe6+ Kd4 2. Qe4+? Sxe4! Solvers may look askance at that curious c6 pawn. It actually holds a prospective flight square after 1. Qc3! (2. Qc5) Kd6 2. Qe5. Self-block comes by 1. ... Bd6 2. Qc4. The knight contributes a riff, 1. ... Se4 2. Qd3.

Each of Black's men conspire to hamstring tries in **448**. 1. Qh4? (2. Qf2) does not reckon with 1. ... Kg2! 1. Sf2? (2. Qxh1) is more sinewy, but 1. ... Bg2! 1. Qg6? (2. Qg1) would steal a march on 1. ... Bg2 2. Qb1, but 1. ... f2! The serene 1. Qf6! has replies for 1. ... Kg2 2. Qxf3, 1. ... Bg2 (or 1. ... Ke1) 2. Qa1, and 1. ... f2 2. Qxf2. The bishop shift of part (b) shuts the doorway to a1. But a new lane opens for 1. Qc6 changing 1. ... Bg2 2. Qc1 and 1. ... f2 2. Qxh1.

SUSHKOV THEME

Threat avoidance has made a thematic splash in recent years. In **449,** 2. Qc3 and 2. Qe3 are both threatened were d5 guarded. 1. Bf3? leaves off watch on c4 to menace only (2. Qc3). Then 1. ... Bc4 brings the "avoided" 2. Qe3, but 1. ... e4! 1. Bb3! (2. Qe3) has 1. ... e4 return 2. Qc3 and there is 1. ... Bc4 2. Qxc4 to boot. Such elements of pseudo le Grand are always present.

450 would have queen chops at d4 and e3 given reinforcement on those points. However, knight arrivals expose flights elsewhere. 1. Sbc2? (only 2. Qd4) Kf4 2. Qe3, but 1. ... c5! 1. Sec2! (only 2. Qe3) Ke5 2. Qd4.

451. M LIPTON
The Problemist,
1995

#2

452. RAL
Original

#2

453. R NOTARO
Probleemblad,
1978

#2

454. R A LINCOLN
Magadanskaya pravda,
1998

#2

455. L SALAI
*Australian Chess Problem
Magazine,* 1996

#2

456. M KERHUEL
Prize e. a., GAMA Ty,
1995

#2 (b) Pg4>g6

457. N ZINOVYEV
Ideal-Mate Review,
1998

#2 Two solutions

458. R A LINCOLN
The Problemist,
1996

#2

459. R A LINCOLN
1st HM., GAMA Ty,
1997

#2 (b) Ra6>e6

SWAPS

Reciprocal relationships can be displayed copiously. A method whereby Black "corrects" and thereby prevents duals is catnip for many composers. **451** must indubitably hold the record for economy. After 1. Kg6, Black's rook is caught in the pincers of 1. ... R~rank 2. Qd6 and 1. ... R~file 2. Qe8. There's no repetition upon 1. ... Re8 2. Qxe8, — not 2. Qd6? Re7! And again with 1. ... Rd6 2. Qxd6, — not 2. Qe8? since it's illegal.

My **452** has pretty much the same thing without a queen. 1. Ba7 R~rank 2. Bc6 and 1. ... R~file 2. Rb8. Duals are averted in identical manner as Lipton's problem — 1. ... Rb8 2. Rxb8 or 1. ... Rc6 2. Bxc6.

453 articulates yet another weary rook situated mid-board. 1. Kf3 prepares 1. ... R~rank 2. Qc3 and 1. ... R~file 2. Qd6. Arrivals at each interface complete the gamut with 1. ... Rd6 2. Qxd6 and 1. ... Rc3 2. Qxc3.

A Black bishop can also be made to jump through the hoops. **454** has two colorless tries easily made defunct by 1. Qh3? (2. Qa3, Qb3) Bf3! and 1. Qh5? (2. Qa5,Qb5) Bd5! An impassive 1. Qh6! awaits with 2. Qa6 for 1. ... B~Southeast, or 2. Qc6 for 1. ... B~Northeast. Captures are required to take in 1. ... Ba6 2. Qxa6 and 1. ... Bc6 2. Qxc6.

The set mates of **455** trade places post-key. White would surely be loath to unsettle 1. ... Kd3 2. Qf3 and 1. ... Kxe4 2. Qe2, but 1. ... b4! is a free agent. So 1. Bd1 (2. Qf3, Qe2) reverses the follow-ups to 1. ... Kd3 2. Qe2 and 1. ... Kxe4 2. Qf3. That coupled menace is a burr in the saddle but largely inevitable with such adjoining flights.

Twinning can competently eliminate recourse to nasty double threats. In the parched topography of **456,** the groggy king limps into two diagonal cells. 1. e5

predicates razor-sharp accuracy for continuations. 1. ... Kc6 2. Qd6 (2. Qe8? Kb6!) and 1. ... Ke6 2. Qe8 (2. Qd6? Kf7!). The alternate portion has 1. c5 parse mates thusly — 1. ... Kc6 2. Qe8 (2. Qd6? Kb5!) and 1. ... Ke6 2. Qd6 (2. Qe8? Kf6!).

White's first and second plays can be swapped in multi-solution format. The quaint **457** trees the bashful possum on discrete squares although White's moves are the same. Juggling their order gives 1. Bg6 Kg5 2. Bf4 or 1. Bf4+ Kh5 2. Bg6. Here's an absolute quintessence of ideal mates.

The switching of try and threat pieces occurs in **458.** 1. Qe5? voyages into enemy waters for (2. Rc7). But this idea is shipwrecked on the shoals of 1. ... Bd5! Therefore, rook makes key and queen the threat by 1. Rb7! (2. Qb5). Now that 1. ... Bd5 bugaboo perishes to 2. Qe8. Two other defenses are relegated to limbo through 1. . . . Bf1 2. Qf3 and 1. . . . Sd4 2. Qc5. The main source of pleasure derived from chess problems does not come from their composition or solving. It comes from meeting fellow hobbyists. I was fortunate enough to make the acquaintance of Jack Gill at a British "weekend." As far as I know, he does not compose, but is gratefully content with appreciating the efforts of others. His genial charm is revealed through a delightfully idiomatic parlance of description. Of this position he wrote: "Her majesty's bid is gazumped, but a crafty rook shemmy compensates the negative equity. "

In **459,** 1. ... Bb2! staves off 1. Qb6? (2. Qb1). Ironically, that defense allows the threat after 1. Qg1! When 1. ... Ka1 2. Rxa3, rook is the mater and queen the pinner. Part (b) has role reversal after 1. Re1 Ka1 2. Qxa3 with queen playing executioner to rook the impaler. This setup has bishop moves tattooed by 2. Qf7.

460. RAL
Original

#2

461. V PILCHENKO
2nd-3rd Prize, *Smena*, 1997

#2

462. J MAYHEW
The Problemist Supplement, 1993

#2

463. S SHEDEY & V LUKANOV
1st Prize, *Chernovy girnik,*1977

#2

464. J HARTONG & K ALBARDA
Probleemblad, 1962

#2

465. R A LINCOLN
The Problemist Supplement, 1999

#2

466. V DYACHUK
Die Schwalbe, 1996

#2

467. W SPECKMANN
Canadian Chess Chat, 1981

#2

468. RAL
Original

#2

SWAPS (CONT'D)

White's bishop and d3-rook share reciprocal functions in **460**. 1. Bf1 pelts either 1. ... e5 or 1. ... Ka6 with a virile 2. Rd5. The former case has the leader acting as Jack Ketch while trailer guards a6. The latter has rearward bishop mating with rook tending to a5. Of course, 1. ... a3 buckles under to 2. Rxa3.

TRANSFER TOKENS

Mate transference is a fixed condition where the same mate occurs after a differing black move. There is frequently some kind of "normal" change that tags along. **461** has a painless, but classy hoax with change and transfer emanating *pari passu*. 1. h5? puts faith in 1. ... gxh5 2. Rxh5 or 1. ... gxf5 2. Bxf5. But Black divests this dud by 1. ... g5! The proper 1. Rh5! uproots an impudent 1. ... g5 with 2. hxg5. 1. ... gxh5 is altered with 2. Bf5 arriving via transfer.

Transference can be nicely wedded to separate Black responses as **462** shows. 2. Bd3 is set for 1. ... c5. A give-and-take 1. Sd5 installs a new mate upon 1. ... c5 2. Qd3. A recursive 2. Bd3 treats either 1. ... cxd5 or 1. ... Kb5. The hyperactive bishop swabs one last driblet, 1. ... Kxd5 2. Bg8.

A pair of flights are duly exchanged in **463**. 1. Kd7? stoops from the vertex depending on 1. ... Kb5 2. Bf1 or 1. ... Kd5 2. Be6. But 1. ... b3! is a wet blanket. So the two-for-two trade goes 1. Qe5! with transfers 2. Bf1 and 2. Be6 pursuing 1. ... b3 (or 1. ... Kd3) and 1. ... Kb3.

Only six men are used for **464**, which is arguably among the best double transfers in the archives. Captures of knight preordain 1. ... gxh6 2. Qf7 (self-block) and 1. ... Kxh6 2. Qh5 (self-injury). The saucy 1. Sg8 returns those mates with 1. ... g6 2. Qf7 (open gate) and 1. ... Rxg8 2. Qh5 (self-block).

Set and try phases are requisite to tuck away double transfers for **465**. 1. ... Kc4 is no concern, because of 2. Qd3. Black's querulous knight declines to cooperate on 1. Bf2? Sd6 2. Rc5, but goes anywhere else. 1. Kd3? hems in c4 and e4 so that "anywhere else" costs 2. Qd7. However, 1. ... Sd6! secures. 1. Bd4! finds a crevice in the armor where 2. Qd3 and 2. Qd7 take their ready encores following 1. ... Kxd4 and 1. ... Kd6. The knight's livelihood sardonically fades with a whimper, 1. ... S~ 2. Qxe5.

TRY AND TRY AGAIN

Tries are the working capital of the modern two-mover. Miniatures show a thematic spectrum as well as their larger brethren. It took a long time before the "old school" was persuaded about the efficacy of ersatz starts. In **466,** White will threaten (2. Qa2) when his bishop vacates the square. 1. Bf7? is too far, 1. ... Se6!, and 1. Bc4? is too close, 1. ... Sb2! 1. Bd5! is just right where defenses are filtered 1. ... Sc1 2. Qxc1 and 1. ... Sb2 2. Qxc5.

Rival queens coexist cheek by jowl in **467.** That curvetting knight makes a fatiguing tour with the common aim of (2. Qb6). 1. Sa8? allows a truculent pin, 1. ... Qxc8! 1. Sc4? heads that off, but 1. ... Bxc4! 1. Sa4? or 1. Sd7?, foreseeing 2. Sc5 when 1. ... Qxc8, get obliterated by the scalawag bishop. The tension abates with 1. Sd5! Qxc8 2. Sb4 and 1. ... Ka7 2. Qxa7.

White's queen enters into a forest primeval in **468.** 1. Qf1+? Kh2 2. Qg2, but 1. ... Kh4! 1. Qxf5+? Kh4 2. Qg4, but 1. ... Kh2! 1. Qe2? (2. Qh5) Be7! 1. Qd5? (2. Qh1) Bd6! 1. Qb8? (2. Qg3) f4! This dim demesne is ultimately pierced with 1. Qe5! (2. Qg3). Black's wan rejoinders are 1. ... f4 2. Qh5, 1. ... Bd6 2. Qh8, and 1. ... Kh4 2. Qh2.

469. Z JANEVSKI
Problem,
1970

#2

470. Y LALUSHKIN
Na smenu!,
1992

#2

471. V HELBELT
1st Prize, *Buletin problemistic,* 1988

#2

472. RAL
Original

#2

473. V DYACHUK
The Problemist,
1994

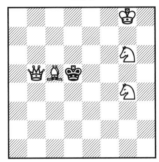

#2

474. RAL
Original

#2

475. V MELNICHENKO
Leninski prapor,
1989

#2

476. R A LINCOLN
StrataGems,
1999

#2

477. V PILCHENKO
Die Schwalbe,
1996

#2

TRY AND TRY AGAIN (CONT'D)

White's queen is engulfed in a vortex of scrumptious leads for **469.** 1. Qa5? will zap 1. ... Kd4 2. Qd2, but 1. ... Sb4! 1. Qb6? (2. Qe3) has 2. Qd4 for 1. ... Kd2, but 1. ... Sc3! 1. Qe7? again scans e3 with 1. ... Kd4 2. Qe5 and 1. ... Kd2 2. Qe2. But this also goes south to that incorrigible 1. ... Sc3! One last tussle with the knight insurgent, 1. Qc7!, coasts to victory over 1. ... S~ 2. Q(x)c3, 1. ... Kd4 2. Qc4, and 1. ... Kd2 2. Qc2. An octet of mates forms a corona-like outline around Black's king.

There is a brief, vigorous tug-of-war between White queen and Black's dinky arsenal in **470.** 1. Qb8? (2. Qe5) plans to defile the self-block 1. ... Bd6 by 2. Qb3. But the bishop demurs with 1. ... Bxd4! instead. 1. Qa5? (2. Qxc5) impounds that defender fast, but 1. ... e5! So the valiant skirmisher assails e5 from another angle, 1. Qh8! Then, 2. Qh1 seduces 1. ... Bd6 while 2. Qxd4 tomahawks 1. ... Bxd4. Almost forgotten in the hectic hubbub is 1. ... Kd6 2. Qd8.

471 has sundry methods whereby the knight attempts to flimflam Black's nimble-witted queen. First, a set 1. ... Qf4 2. Bd4 should be filed for reference. 1. Sd6?, with a focal clench on c4 and f5, can now be met by the safe 1. ... Qf4! In like manner, 1. Sd2? leers at c4 and f1 — ditto, 1. ... Qf4! A bald threat, 1. Sg5? (2. Qd2), wishes for 1. ... Qd7 2. Qf3, but 1. ... Qd5! Only 1. Sg3! (2. Qe2) can emasculate that bastion of strength. Three defenses are purged 1. ... Qf3 2. Qd2, 1. ... Qf2 2. Qe4, and 1. ... Qf1 2. Sxf1. This sprawl epitomizes a fair day's work.

White inducts the same cadre in **472,** Black getting by with thinner assets. Again, knight tittups provide the interest. 1. Sb3?, spattering multi-threats, is hobbled 1. ... Sxb3! 1. Se6? (2. Qd4) looks smarter as 1. ... Sb3 collapses to 2. Qxb3, but 1. ... c5! Surely the evil double threat of 1. Se4? (2. Sd2,Qc3) wins? — nay, 1. ...

c6! One last pirouette, 1. Sd7! (2. Se5), redeems the chips upon 1. ... c6 2. Sb6.

A Dombrovskis-like scuffle occurs in **473.** 1. S6e5? (2. Qc6,Qc4) has 2. Qd7 for 1. ... Ke6, but 1. ... Ke4! eludes. Similarly, 1. S4e5? (same threats) goes 2. Qd3 upon 1. ... Ke4, but 1. ... Ke6! The violence is counterproductive, so a tranquil 1. Sh4! hunkers down. Then the swallows come back to Capistrano with 1. ... Ke6 2. Qc6 and 1. ... Ke4 2. Qc4.

474 is somehow vaguely reminiscent of the foregoing. 1. Se1? peppers both 1. ... e4 2. Sf4 and 1. ... Ke4 2. Qxe5, but not 1. ... Ke6! 1. S2h4? asserts 2. Qc6 against 1. ... Ke6, but 1. ... Ke4! 1. S6h4! controls king flights precisely the same way as in Vasyl Dyachuk's position. A further boon is 1. ... e4 2. Sf4.

Two hazy apparitions nearly trap the Black bishop of **475.** 1. Rc5? B~ 2. Qe7, but 1. ... Be4! 1. Qc3? B~ 2. Qc7, but 1. ... Rc8! 1. Qc1! ambushes anew for the 2. Qc7 finish, and now 2. Qg5 mortifies 1. ... Rc8. Other shards are 1. ... Kc8 2. Re8 and 1. ... R~ 2. R(x)b8.

White disgorges a boatload of ten mates across four phases in **476.** 1. Qg6? (2. Qg7,Qg8) goes astray since 1. ... Sxc6! 1. Qd7? (2. Qe8) deceives 1. ... Sd6 2. Qe7, but not 1. ... Sxf7! 1. Sxd8? lays low that awful tyrant and waits on 1. ... S~ 2. Qc5, 1. ... Se7 2. Sd6. But that other crusty cohort has an ace up his sleeve, 1. ... Sd6! 1. Se5! champions (2. Sg6) where both Black knights and king generate byplay through 1. ... Sxf7 2. Qxf7, 1. ... Se7 2. Sd7, and 1. ... Ke7 2. f8=Q.

477 has another cantankerous knight practice his innings. 1. Qc4? Sb3 2. Qb5, but 1. ... Sc2! 1. Rc4? Sc2 2. Qxc2, but 1. ... Sb3! A *coup de fors*, 1. Rc3!, retires 1. ... S~ 2. Q(x)b3 while tries are salvaged for 1. ... bxc3 2. Qc4 and 1. ... b3 2. Rc4.

478. V MARKOVSKY
Zemlya Balty,
1995

#2

479. RAL
Original

#2

480. M SCHRECKENBACH
Sächsische Zeitung,
1993

#2

481. V MELNICHENKO
1st-2nd Prize, *Smena,*
1995

#2

482. R A LINCOLN
The Problemist,
1999

#2

483. B ZHEZHERUN
Kudesnik,
1998

#2 (b) Turn 90º
counterclockwise

484. R A LINCOLN
The Problemist,
1992

#2 (b) Turn 180º

485. R A LINCOLN
(v) *The Problemist Supplement,*
1992

#2 (b) Turn 180º

486. N ZINOVYEV
Ideal-Mate Review,
1991

#2 (b) Turn 90º clockwise

TRY AND TRY AGAIN (CONT'D)

A rambunctious rook forces White to winnow the chaff in **478.** 1. Scb6? (2. Sd5) has one line-cut covered 1. ... Ra3 2. Qc4, but nothing for 1. ... Rb3! 1. Sa5? (2. Sc6) addresses 1. ... Rb3 2. Qxb3, but the cagey scamp hits upon 1. ... Rc3! The other knight hangs the coonskin on the wall by 1. Sab6! (2. Sd5). The 1. ... Rb3 barrier brings 2. Qa5 and 1. ... Rxd4 waives 2. Qa3.

The play of **479** is not exactly a barnburner, but White does leech every ounce from those "possibles." 1. Qb6? (2. Qb7, Qb8) wafts a trial balloon which is punctured by 1. ... b1=Q! Hence, the knight will pivot to threaten (2. Qa7). 1. Sc6? blockades the diagonal so that 1. ... f2! Likewise, 1. Sc8? bars topmost row for 1. ... Se3! 1. Sb5! is hunky-dory after 1. ... f2 2. Qxg2 and 1. ... Se3 2. Qg8.

In **480,** White's rook hikes about the countryside, trusting like Mr. Micawber, that something will turn up. 1. Rd5? (2. Bg6) Kf7! 1. Rf5? (2. Ba4) Kd7! 1. Rc5? Kd7 2. Ba4, but 1. ... Kd7! 1. Rb6? Kf7 2. Bg6, but 1. ... Kd7! The sagacious 1. Ba4! (2. Rf5) uses one try for the threat and another as a variation to nab 1. ... Kd7 2. Rc5.

One preliminary from **481** is rather punk. 1. Ba4? (2. Qc2) changes a set 1. ... Kc4 2. Qc2 to 2. Qb3, but 1. ... Ke4! snickers. 1. Kf3? contemplates 1. ... B~ 2. B(x)b5 and 1. ... Bc4 2. Be4. It may take a moment before one discerns that scorpion sting, 1. ... Bb7! The garland goes to 1. Ke1! (2. Qb3) where 1. ... Bc4 (or 1. ... Ke3) are bludgeoned 2. Qd2.

482 sees the queen wage a laborious campaign with negative repercussions. All of these tries intend (2. Qxd7). 1. Qg7? lets the king run away 1. ... Kd5! The improved 1. Qd4? has 1. ... S~ 2. Qf6, but 1. ... Se5! 1. Qb5? will plant 2. Qe8 upon 1. ... S~, but 1. ... Sf6! 1. Qb7? brings 2. Rc6 or 2. Re4 following 1. ... S~. One fix,

1. ... Se5 2. f5, must be shunned, but the other, 1. ... Sc5! is a vindicator. With a devious 1. Rc7!, the wheel is broken at the cistern. Pin mates monitor 1. ... Ke7 (or 1. ... Kf7) 2. Qf6 and 1. ... Kd6 (or 1. ... Kd5) 2. Qe5. The multiples which tail 1. ... S~ cannot be regulated.

TURN FOR THE BETTER

Board turns can effectively jazz up positions by causing pawns to move in other directions. Try and key often split off in a mummery of musical chairs. **483** employs dubious tactics by merely blocking Black's outlying pawn, yet there are invigorating changes. 1. Qg6 harasses the abject king with 1. ... Kb3 2. Qc2 and 1. ... Ka5 2. Sc3. After rotation, 1. Qb6 uses a new fulcrum to lacerate 1. ... Kf2 2. Re4 and 1. ... Kd1 2. Qb1.

For **484,** White inspects 1. Qg6? (2. Qe8) Bc6 2. Qxc6 and 1. ... a6 2. Qxa6, but 1. ... Bb7! A harsh 1. Qg2? (2. Qxf3) disregards 1. ... a6! 1. Bg2! (2. Bxf3) will waylay the somber bishop somewhere along the diagonal. (b) also has a try, 1. Bb7? (2. Bxc6) b1=Q! This time, 1. Qb7! (2. Qxc6) grabs hold of bishop while watching 1. ... b1=Q 2. Qxb1.

485 was published without the twinning proviso. Both try and key threaten (2. Qc2). 1. Qe2? cannot handle 1. ... a2! 1. Qe4! arrives like a ravenous buzzard ready to feast on 1. ... Bh7 2. Qc4, 1. ... a2 2. Qb4, 1. ... Kc3 2. Qe3, and 1. ... Ka2 2. Qb1. I later optimized with full revolution. Then, 1. Qd5? loses to 1. ... h5!, whereas 1. Qd7! changes two aspects — 1. ... a5 2. Qg7 and 1. ... Kb5 2. Qg4.

Under promotion by pawn on first and second move is fleshed out wondrously in **486** 1. c8=B tugs the brooding king into 1. ... Kc6 2. Bd7. The flip side has 1. g7 Kf6 2. g8=S. A persnickety kvetch would wag the finger at those thieving magpies which take flights.

487. **RAL**
Original

#2 (b) Turn 90º
counterclockwise

488. **R A LINCOLN**
The Problemist,
1992

#2 (b) Turn 90º
counterclockwise

489. **V MARKS**
Comm., Krumm MT,
1998

#2 (b) Turn 90º clockwise
(c) Turn 180º
(d) Turn 270º clockwise

490. **RAL**
Original

#2

491. **R A LINCOLN**
Newark Star-Ledger,
1998

#2

492. **V PILCHENKO**
6th-7th Prize, Bron MT,
1992

#2

493. **P BENKO**
Chess Life,
1980

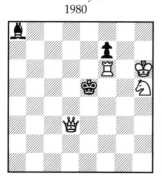

#2

494. **RAL**
Original

#2

495. **RAL**
Original

#2

TURN FOR THE BETTER (CONT'D)

Black's men are clumped holus-bolus in **487** making a decorative visual icon. White must hoist his stagnant knight from the cellar to either b3 or e2. The object of guarding d4 is to prevent that suzerain's escape, *i.e.* 1. ... Ke4 2. Qf3. 1. Sb3? has no say on 1. ... e4!, but 1. Se2! can continue, 1. ... e4 2. Sf4. One quarter turn has 1. Sg5? cave in where another shrinking violet comes forth — 1. ... c3! 1. Sf2! agreeably makes 2. Qf4 liable for 1. ... c3.

In **488,** 1. Sd7? (2. Sb8) has 1. ... d5 2. Qc5, but gets a fat goose egg when 1. ... Rb4! 1. Sd5! catches Black in the coils of guarding both 2. Sb4 and 2. e8=Q — impossible. After the axis shifts, 1. Sd4? is silly as the rook merely hacks along the file. So the stormy petrel, 1. Sb4! (2. Sa2), returns with gusto to chill 1. ... Re2 2. Sd5.

This miniature tourney was held in memory of Hans-Christoph Krumm, respected editor of the *Deutsche Schachblätter* and *Schach-Report*. Positions had to contain White rook, bishop, knight, and pawn. Black was limited to one pawn. An entrant was shown previously which twinned by moving pieces about (# 297). **489** expands to four adaptations through a lazy susan twirl of the board. (a) 1. Ka5 Kc5 2. Rc2 and 1. ... Kb3 2. Bd5. (b) 1. Bg3 Kd4 2. Bf2 and 1. ... Ke2 (or 1. ... d4) 2. Re5. (c) 1. g8=Q (2. Rf7) (d) 1. b8=Q+ Kd7 2. Rb7. Admittedly, those queen promotions are no great shakes, but this is still a twinning extravaganza.

UNKIND CUTS

Defensive impediments on White lines find many applications. In **490,** a knight clashes with Black's redoubtable guardians. 1. Sxd5? (2. Sf6, Sc3) Bd4! 1. Sb5? (2. Sc3) Bd4 2. Qxd4, but 1. ... d4! These same refutations are worthless as line-cuts when 1. Bf4! threatens (2. Qxd5)

— 1. ... d4 2. Qe2 and 1. ... Bd4 2. Qc2. The supple bishop produces one more sliver, 1. ... Bxc7 2. Qe3.

491 has a similar premise, but lacks the vestige of a try. 1. Bc5 (2. Qf5) rowels Black's defense to 1. ... Bd6 2. Qxd6 and 1. ... d6 2. Qe4. 1. ... Be5 slices the fifth rank so 2. Qf5+? Kd5!, but self-blocks for 2. Qxd7.

Vyacheslav Pilchenko is one of the towering pillars of today's miniature. **492** is an opaque mystery with pseudo le Grand effects. In this area, he has few peers. Both White knights spar with that Black bishop brigand. 1. Sbd4? (2. Qc6) has 1. ... Bc5 sever a line for 2. Qe6, but 1. ... Bc7! 1. Sfd4! (2. Qe6) involves yet another cut/block with 1. ... Be5 2. Qc6. 1. ... Ke5 (or 1. ... Ke4) 2. Qf5 round out a snazzy pageant.

White can sacrifice his rook with haughtiness in **493.** 1. Sg7? (2. Rf5) has 2. Qd6 for 1. ... Be4, but 1. ... Bd5! nicks incisively. 1. Sg3! (2. Qd6) welcomes a rerun of 1. ... Bd5 as 2. Qc3 concludes. The Promethean chess talents of Pal Benko have brightened many spheres. A former world champion contender, he is also an outstanding problemist and journalist. His "Endgame Lab" has long been a popular feature in *Chess Life*.

494 has 1. Kg7 edge closer to Black king's bailiwick menacing (2. Qa8). Were the d7 urchin to vanish, White could choose 2. Qe6 or 2. Qa4. Precise separation is elicited from 1. ... d6 2. Qe6 and 1. ... d5 2. Qa4. One hysterical grasp for a straw is 1. ... Sa3 2. Qe2.

Two tries of note in **495** are 1. Bd5? (2. Qc4) Se6! and 1. Qe2? (multi-threats) d6! A waiting stance is the better part of valor. So 1. Qg7! defers provocations for 1. ... d6 2. Qb7 (2. Qc7?) and 1. ... d5 2. Qc7 (2. Qb7?). 1. ... S~ 2. Qxd7 is the whole kit and caboodle.

496. A & V LEBEDEV
Die Schwalbe,
1993

#2

497. RAL
Original

#2

498. A KUZOVKOV
1st Prize, Bron MT,
1991

#2

499. M PARRINELLO
The Problemist,
1985

#2

500. M SUBOTIC
3rd Prize, *Sahovska
Kompozicija,* 1992

#2

501. RAL
Original

#2

502. RAL
Original

#2

503. RAL
Original

#2

503. RAL
Original

#2

VALVES

This defensive slipup opens a Black line of influence while simultaneously closing another. #276 showed the king executing such a *faux pas*. These examples have pawns toggling the on-off switch. **496** is probably the only extant archetype that utilizes a Black queen. 1. Qc2 (2. Qg6) can be defended 1. ... e5 which shrouds a diagonal for 2. Qh2.

497 actuates one piece while shutting off an accomplice — the "bi-valve." The pinchbeck key, 1. Kf8 (2. Qg8), causes bishops to fumble 1. ... d4 2. Qg7. This little mock-up wrings a collateral 1. ... h5 2. Qxh5.

ZAGORUYKO

This change system was recounted already in # 238. As Zagoruykos go, **498** is quite frankly a lollapalooza. Five of Black's six "thematic" moves self-block. The sets are 1. ... Be5 2. Qc4 and 1. ... Re4 2. Qd6. 1. Qf5? (2. e3) would deign to answer 1. ... Be5 2. Qd3 or 1. ... Re4 2. Qc5, but 1. ... Rh3! 1. Sc3! (2. Sb5) comes like a bayonet from the scabbard to allocate 1. ... Be5 2. Qb6 and 1. ... Re4 2. Qxe4.

There is a saccharine demitasse of alterations for **499**. 1. Qg5? has 1. ... B~ 2. Qa4 and 1. ... Ba2 2. Qd4, but is silenced 1. ... Bf5! A derivative 1. Qg4? turns out 1. ... B~ 2. Qa4 and 1. ... Ba2 2. Ba2. Qd4, but Black intromits a callous 1. ... Be4! 1. Bc4! enervates the jocund bishop by the supervenient 1. ... B~ (or 1. ... Ka2) 2. Qa7 and 1. ... Ba2 2. f7.

The "4x2" changes of **500,** are by comparison, a Titan's goblet. 1. Qg7? quashes 1. ... Ka2 2. Qa7 and 1. ... Ba2 2. f7, but 1. ... Bxc2! 1. Qg5? would dissolve 1. ... Ka2 2. Qa5 and 1. ... Ba2 2. Qe5, but 1. ... Bxc2! With 1. Qg4?, the circus goes on as more clowns somersault out of the coupe, 1. ... Ka2 2. Qa4 and 1. ... Ba2 2. Qd4. Again, 1. ... Bxc2! is the snag. At last, 1. Qf3! and the punch-drunk lemmings leap into the sea 1. ... Ka2 (or 1. ... Bxc2) 2. Qa3 and 1. ... Ba2 2. Qc3.

APPENDIX

Most of the appended problems are of middling quality and deserve no comment. But some respectable bits can be found. I bid the gentle reader to dig out those diamonds in the rough!

501.
1. Ba7	(2. Qb6)
1. ... b5	2. Qxa3
1. ... Rb3	2. Qa4
1. ... Kxa7	2. Qxb7

502.
1. Kg4	(2. Qd4)
1. ... Rd5	2. Qxd5
1. ... Rxc4	2. Qf5
1. ... Ke5	2. Qe7

503.
1. Sf3	(2. Qg5)
1. ... h6	2. Qf5
1. ... Ra5	2. Bf7
1. ... Rg6	2. Qh4

504.
1. Qc1	(2. Qc2)
1. ... B~Northeast	2. Qe3
1. ... B~Northwest	2. Qc3
1. ... e1=S	2. Qd1

505. RAL
Original

#2

506. RAL
Original

#2

507. RAL
Original

#2

508. RAL
Original

#2

509. RAL
Original

#2

510. RAL
Original

#2

511. RAL
Original

#2

512. RAL
Original

#2

513. RAL
Original

#2

505.

1. ... e5	2. Bc8
1. Bf1?	(2. Bh3)
1. ... g5!	
1. Be2!	
1. ... g5	2. Bg4
1. ... e5	2. Qg4
1. ... e3	2. Bd3

506.

1. ... e5	2. Qf6
1. Qe2?	e6!
1. Qc4!	
1. ... e6	2. Qf4
1. ... e5	2. Qg4
1. ... g5	2. Qe4
1. ... Ke5	2. Qd5

507.

1. Qb8	
1. ... g3	2. Qf4
1. ... S~	2.Q(x)h2
1. ... Sg3	2. Qd8

508.

1. Qf2	(2. Bf5)
1. ... Bh3	2. Qf3
1. ... Se7	2. Qd4
1. ... Kd3	2. Qe2

509.

1. Bb3?	
1. ... Kf5	2. Qh5
1. ... Kf3	2. Bd1
1. ... S~!	
1. Be8!	(2. Qh5)
1. ... Sf4	2. Se3
1. ... Kf5	2. Qh3
1. ... Kf3	2. Bh5

510.

1. ... f3	2. Qe3
1. Bc5?	
1. ... Kd3	2. Qc2
1. ... Sd5!	
1. Bc3!	(2. Qe2)
1. ... f3	2. Qd4
1. ... Sd5	2. Bc2
1. ... Kd3	2. Qf3

511.

1. Bc4	(2. Qd5)
1. ... Sb4	2. Qe3
1. ... Se7	2. Qf4
1. ... Kf3	2. Bd5

512.

1. Ke8	(2. Qe5)
1. ... Sd5	2. Qc6
1. ... g5	2. Rh6
1. ... Kf6	2. Qf5
1. ... Kd6	2. Qd7

513.

1. Qb7	
1. ... a6	2. Qd7
1. ... a5	2. Ba7
1. ... axb6	2. Qxb6

514. RAL
Original

#2

515. RAL
Original

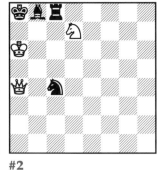

#2

516. RAL
Original

#2

517. RAL
Original

#2

518. RAL
Original

#2

519. RAL
Original

#2

520. RAL
Original

#2

521. RAL
Original

#2

522. RAL
Original

#2

514.

1. Sg6	(2. Qe5)
1. ... d6	2. Qf7
1. ... d5	2. Bc8
1. ... Kf5	2. Qxd7

515.

1. Qb5	(2. Qb7)
1. ... Rc7	2. Qxb8
1. ... Rc6+	2. Qxc6
1. ... Sa5	2. Sb6

516.

1. Qf2	
1. ... S~	2. B(x)f5
1. ... d4	2. Qf3
1. ... Kd3	2. Sc5

517.

1. c4?	(2. Qb5)
1. ... Sxc4!	
1. Sa3?	(2. Qb5)
1. ... Bxa3!	
1. c3!	(2. Qxb4)
1. ... B~	2. Qa6
1. ... Ba5	2. Qc6
1. ... Bxc3	2. Sxc3

518.

1. Kc3	
1. ... S~	2. Q(x)c6
1. ... Kc5	2. Ra5
1. ... Kxa4	2. Qa6

519.

1. Qe2?	
1. ... g2	2. Qg4
1. ... h1=Q!	
1. Qd5?	g2!
1. Qe1!	(2. Qxg3)
1. ... h1=S	2. Qxh1
1. ... Kg2	2. Rxg3
1. ... Kxh4	2. Rh6

520.

1. Qc1	(2. Qa3)
1. ... c3	2. Qf4
1. ... Kxa4	2. Qxc4

521.

1. ... Kh4	2. Qxh2
1. Sf1?	(2. Qg3)
1. ... Bf4!	
1. Sh5?	(2. Qg3)
1. ... h1=S!	
1. Se2!	(2. Qg3)
1. ... Bf4	2. Sxf4
1. ... h1=S	2. Sg1

522.

1. Bf6	
1. ... Sf~	2. B(x)g6
1. ... Se~	2. Rb8
1. ... Sd8	2. Re7

523. RAL
Original

#2

524. RAL
Original

#2

525. RAL
Original

#2

526. RAL
Original

#2

527. RAL
Original

#2

528. RAL
Original

#2

529. RAL
Original

#2

530. RAL
Original

#2

531. RAL
Original

#2

523.

1. Qc5?	(2. Qf8)
1. ... a6!	
1. Qa4!	
1. ... a6	2. Qxa6
1. ... a5	2. Qxa5
1. ... c5	2. Qe8
1. ... S~	2. Qxc6

524.

1. Qf6?	(2. Qg5)
1. ... Be3!	
1. Qd2?	(2. Qg5)
1. ... Kh4!	
1. Qf4!	(2. Qg5)
1. ... Be3	2. Qh2
1. ... Sg6	2. Rh7
1. ... Kh4	2. Qxg4

525.

1. Bf6?	(2. Qd8)
1. ... Bd7!	
1. Bh4?	(2. Qd8)
1. ... Sxh4!	
1. Bg5!	(2. Qd8)
1. ... Bd7	2. Qxg6
1. ... Se7	2. Qxe7
1. ... Sb7	2. Qxc6

526.

1. Qh6?	
1. ... f5	2. Se5
1. ... g5!	
1. Qh2!	
1. ... f5	2. f3
1. ... g5	2. Sh6
1. ... Kf5	2. Qh3

527.

1. Se3	(2. Qg4)
1. ... Sf6	2. Qe5
1. ... Bxd4	2. Qf5
1. ... Kxd4	2. Qd5

528.

1. Qc2?	(2. Qxb2)
1. ... a3!	
1. Bd4!	
1. ... a3	2. Sc3
1. ... b1=Q	2. Qxa4
1. ... b1=S	2. Qc2

529.

1. Sh5?	
1. ... gxh5!	
1. Se2	
1. ... g5	2. Qc8
1. ... Kxh3	2. Qg3
1. ... Kf5	2. Qf4

530.

1. Kf5?	
1. ... exd3	2. Qe5
1. ... e3!	
1. Qd2!	
1. ... exd3	2. Qf4
1. ... e3	2. Qc3
1. ... Ke5	2. d4

531.

1. Qc5	(2. Qf5)
1. ... Se5	2. Qd4
1. ... d5	2. Qe3
1. ... Kd3	2. Qc2

532. RAL
Original

#2

533. RAL
Original

#2

534. RAL
Original

#2

535. RAL
Original

#2

536. RAL
Original

#2

537. RAL
Original

#2

538. RAL
Original

#2

539. RAL
Original

#2

540. RAL
Original

#2

532.

1. Qb2?	(2. Qg2)
1. ... Bf2!	
1. Rh3?	
1. ... B~	2. Qa8
1. ... Bd8!	
1. Qa8?	(2. Rh3, Rf2)
1. ... Kxh2!	
1. Rg3!	
1. ... B~	2. Rg1
1. ... Bxg3	2. hxg3
1. ... Kxh2	2. Qxh4

533.

1. Sc3	(2. Qd5)
1. ... Sxc3	2. Qc5
1. ... d6	2. Qb5
1. ... Kd6	2. Qf6

534.

1. Rg5	(2. Qxc4)
1. ... Sc~	2. Q(x)e5
1. ... Sf3	2. Rg4
1. ... Kd4	2. Qd5
1. ... Kf4	2. Qf5

535.

1. Qd5?	(2. Qc4)
1. ... b5	2. Qxa8
1. ... Rc8!	
1. Qd3!	(2. Qc4)
1. ... b5	2. Qa3
1. ... Rc8	2. Qa6
1. ... Sc2	2. Qb3

536.

1. Qc5?	(2. Qb4)
1. ... Kb3!	
1. Qf7?	
1. ... Ka5	2. Qa7
1. ... c5!	
1. Qe2!	
1. ... a2	2. Qxa2
1. ... c5	2. Qb5
1. ... Ka5	2. Qa6
1. ... Kb3	2. Qc2

537.

1. Bd5?	(2. Bxf3)
1. ... f2!	
1. Ra2?	Sc2!
1. Rb2!	
1. ... f2	2. Be2
1. ... Sc2	2. Rb1
1. ... Sb3	2. Bxb3

538.

1. Bg4	(2. Qd4)
1. ... Be5	2. Qf3
1. ... Se2	2. Qf5
1. ... Kd5	2. Qe6

539.

1. Sg3	(2. Qf5)
1. ... Sh3	2. Qe2
1. ... Kf2	2. Qf1
1. ... Kg4	2. Qh5

540.

1. Rc4	
1. ... S~	2. Q(x)f4
1. ... B~	2. Q(x)f2
1. ... h2	2. Qg4
1. ... Kh2	2. Qg1
1. ... Kf3	2. Qd3

INDEX OF COMPOSERS
Numbers refer to problems. Parentheses indicate a joint composition.

INDEX OF COMPOSERS
Numbers refer to problems. Parentheses indicate a joint composition.

Whether you play chess for fun or chess for blood...

Whether you're a casual player or a tournament veteran... You're invited to join America's coast-to-coast chess club! *We're the U.S. Chess Federation, with over 85,000 members of all ages — from beginners to grandmasters.*

U.S. Chess Federation membership offers many benefits:

- The right to earn a national rating
- Big discounts on chess merchandise
- A national magazine packed with information
- An official membership card
- The right to play in local, regional, and national tournaments
- The right to play officially rated chess by mail

FREE— An introductory chess course by nationally renowned chess teacher Bruce Pandolfini and IM Larry Evans

✓ Yes! Enroll me as follows:

- ❐ Adult $40/year.   ❐ Senior *(age 65 or older)* $30/year
- ❐ Youth *(age 19 and under; includes monthly* Chess Life*)* $17/year
- ❐ Scholastic *(age 14 and under; includes bimonthly* School Mates*)* $12/year
- ❐ Also, I want my FREE copy of Basic Chess Curriculum (a $6.00 value).

Check or money order enclosed, in the amount of $_____or charge it.

Credit card number_____ Expiration date _____

Authorized signature _____Daytime telephone _____

Name _____Address _____

City _____ State _____ ZIP _____

Birthdate _____ ❐ Male   ❐ Female

Call toll free: 800-388-KING (5464) Please mention Dept. 30 when responding.
FAX: 914-561-CHES (2437) or **Visit our website at http://www.uschess.org.**
Mail: U.S. Chess Federation, Dept. 30, 3054 Route 9W, New Windsor, NY 12553
Note: Membership dues are not refundable. Canada: Add $6/yr. for magazine postage & handling. Other foreign: Add $15/yr.